MARKED FOR

DESTRUCTION

BY: John Caravella

*William & Marjorie:
The Best of everything to a couple of great people.
Love you both,*

MARKED FOR DESTRUCTION

PUBLISHED BY:

JP PRODUCTS
8823 NW 19th LANE
GAINESVILLE, FL 32606-6765
(352) 332-0904

e-mail adelesdiary@juno.com
web site www.MarkedForDestruction.com

(*Confirm current contact information at Web Site*)

LIBRARY OF CONGRESS CONTROL NUMBER: 2001116587

ISBN 0-9708547-8-1

SECOND EDITION

PRINTED IN THE UNITED STATES OF AMERICA

DEDICATION

This book, and the lessons that may be learned from its pages, is dedicated to all current and aspiring legal guardians, lawyers, and judges of current and prospective Wards. The classrooms on ethics, or your continuing education classes, may just benefit from the experiences your peers have allowed me to endure. Do not use this book as a "how-to-abuse guide;" remember, someday you will be accountable.

I must also include a dedication to my loving and caring friends who made it possible for me to regain my freedom to tell this story. A well-hatched plan having me disappear from existence to drain my assets dry nearly succeeded except for the grit and determination of a few non-professionals. There is also one lone and brave professional, an attorney with the same determination, who helped me at no cost; and he is greatly appreciated.

In addition, I must also dedicate this lesson to all of us who may, at one point in our lives, be faced with decisions about our sunset years. You may come close to where I have been and not even realize what could be happening to you.

My imprisonment was born within the imaginations of greed-driven professionals who relied upon the system to not pay attention to either their actions or their motives. The system is overloaded with their business, but someone must start paying attention.

This is not going to be a long book, so please read it. This could be you.

Adele Fraulen

1935

This book is printed with large type for easy reading.

Please contact us for information about:

☑ Obtaining copies of this book in soft cover.

☑ Ordering this book bound with heavy coil to lie flat while open.

PUBLISHED BY:

JP PRODUCTS
8823 NW 19th LANE
GAINESVILLE, FL 32606-6765
(352) 332-0904

e-mail   adelesdiary@juno.com
web site   **www.MarkedForDestruction.com**

(Confirm current contact information at Web Site)

Second Edition

CONTENTS

CHAPTER 7.

CHRIS TO THE RESCUE..

CHAPTER 8.

THE LAST DAYS...............

REPORTS

INTRODUCTION

This story is about a very kind and sincere senior lady who became dear to me. Being able to contribute to this book is, for me, an honor that has resulted from knowing this gentle lady. I met Adele Fraulen through the desperation of her friends who had committed themselves to rescuing her from an abusive situation. Professionals appointed to her care were to blame.

Adele's large and recent inheritance made her seek professional help for its management, but instead these professionals saw her as an easy "mark." As seen through Adele's eyes, this book recounts their activities and outlines their actions to embezzle her life and her money. Certainly their hope was that no one would notice or, much less, care. They were wrong.

Adele was forced to live the life of a prisoner as her world was quietly stolen from her piece-by-piece. The inexcusable conduct of these professionals started with a lie to obtain a court order so they could be in her life -- to facilitate their plans to remove *all* her social freedoms.

Once that first goal had been accomplished, their remaining schemes took on a freewheeling strategy headed toward a horrifying conclusion. So Adele's future was inevitable, and probably just routine enough for a court never to notice. But her friends noticed.

I came to know Adele because of the pleading of one friend -- and neighbor. This man persisted in telling me about Adele's trouble until I couldn't help but become involved. If for no other reason, I felt compelled to investigate to determine if such a thing could happen in today's world. Unfortunately, I learned that the events he reported to me were true. And, to my complete disgust, I saw these professionals proclaim their fraud to have court approval.

I could not resist the compelling urge to help this woman and expose those who had schemed to steal her from our society.

Adele is free today, but she will probably never recover from her experience. Life is fragile, and it is unfortunate that there will always be those who will take every opportunity to inflict harm upon others.

This time -- Adele was the "mark."

Jack Carerra : **CONTRIBUTING AUTHOR**
04/30/99

I have a story to tell even though I'm nearly 80 years old. I'm tired, and I really don't know if I have time left in my life to tell it. But some things just have to be done, and my hope is that my experience will help someone. After all, that's what we are supposed to do. My name is Adele Fraulen.

I've been single most of my life except for a brief marriage that didn't interest my husband. Early on in our marriage he thought *two* women in his life would make him happier, but I didn't agree. So an early divorce left me single once again and I stayed that way for the rest of my life. I don't think I'll be getting a marriage proposal any time soon.

My life has been relatively quiet and peaceful, and after retiring from my job many years ago, I moved to the coast. I worked my career in administration at a large university in the Midwest. I have a good education and I enjoyed putting it to use in what turned out to be a very rewarding job. But I LOVE my retirement.

So now it's just my dog Bailie and me. I hope nothing happens to her for a long time. She's a good girl. She gives me a reason to get up in the morning and a reason to get out and meet people. Bailie and I go walking many times during the day, and everyone says she's so cute. She's a cottony-white Westie terrier, and I think everyone loves her big dark eyes and her black button-sized nose.

My car has no dents, and I'm very proud of my clean driving record. Bailie loves to go driving with me and I'm really happy that everyone else does, too. If my age makes them scared to ride along, I'm thankful they're kind enough not to show it. Believe it or not, I do watch behind me as I drive just to see that I'm not leaving a wake of destruction. But I think I drive pretty well. So, now, every time you see a little white head of hair poking over the back of a driver's seat, remember, it's not Bailie, but it could be me.

Family? Well, this begins my story. I have one brother, Bob, who lives close by, but we really don't see each other that much. He's pretty sick, his wife is, too, and his son Bobby Jr. lives who-knows-where. My older brother James died recently and left us an estate of nearly one million dollars. I now tend to regret that.

Bob and I are to get its earned interest until we die, and then the estate goes to his Alma Mater. It's a pretty fair arrangement. But what do I do with all this new income? I'm worried some about being in a whole new tax bracket. Should I? At my age?

I'm always able to pay all my bills on time. My birthday is February 3rd...maybe for a present on my *big 80* I'll ask that I stop getting bills? But, even at almost 80 years old, bills still come in. There's the home insurance, the car insurance, the utility bills, the condominium fees; and I take pride in making sure they all get paid in full and on time. I keep my checkbook balanced monthly, and keeping track of finances, at my age, can be a hobby all by itself. I still manage to do some antique collecting, along with other small items, and I have fun passing them on to friends and neighbors. Some things I buy through the mail and from time-to-time I'll mail something to a friend without their expecting it. I like it when I get things in the mail, so I'm sure they do, too.

Now back to my car -- my vehicle of freedom. I hope I never lose it. I'm figuring I have another 20 years of good driving left in me. My car gets me to the stores, the vet for Bailie and other places I like to go. And it provides me an opportunity to take my friends, who don't drive, out for an afternoon. The girls and I get together every now-and-then for lunch, but when they can't go, I just go myself. Everyone at the restaurant and vet's office and bank knows me by name. It's nice to have friends around town and I would miss not seeing them all.

As far as this money thing goes, I know I have enough of my own -- what with stocks and all. And my stockbroker's office is right nearby. But now I have to deal with even more income? I really don't know what to do.

My brother isn't going to be much help to me. And what about his son? Well, personally, I don't think he's very nice. I know that's not nice to say, but he's borrowed money from me some time ago and he's never paid me back. Never even offered. I don't know if I expected him to or not, but I turned him down when he came to me a second time. I know he's *borrowed* enough from his father and, except for when he wants money, I never hear from Bobby Jr.

I have a close friend and neighbor I've known for probably a decade or more. His name is Chris and his wife's name is Patricia. Chris is also the president of our condominium association. They are both very nice. Maybe Chris would be able to help me with some advice?

I saw Chris yesterday and explained my money problem. He was very kind to listen, but said that such a matter was beyond his knowledge. He thought it best, if I have financial questions, to maybe consider seeing my stockbroker or banker.

I thought that was a pretty good idea; and Chris even offered to come with me if I wanted him to. So I made an appointment with the stockbroker for the next day and asked Chris to come along. I drove.

You know, he's no spring chicken either, but he always seems to enjoy the ride. Either I still drive ok or he needs new glasses. Anyway, I always enjoy the freedom of my car and Chris is at least a good sport.

It turned out to be an informative session at the broker's office, yet this is all very confusing to me. The stockbroker said he knows of a professional guardian who can oversee my money affairs and asked if I would like to meet that person?

I guess it wouldn't hurt, as long as I'm looking for help, and Chris said he would be happy to sit in on that meeting, too. So the broker made a phone call or two; and a meeting is all set up at my house for the day after tomorrow.

Oh yes, one other note; Chris and Patricia and my neighbors held a very nice birthday party for me the other day. We all had a good time just being together. As the years go by, being together is much more important to me than anything else. There certainly aren't any *things* I need. Boy, the years are going by so fast....

CHAPTER 3. PROFESSIONAL HELP

FEBRUARY 24, '97

Today is over. I hope I did the right thing. This guardian, Freda Luelow, came with a friend of hers who's an attorney, and some other lady who didn't say much. I think her name was Margaret something. I was glad Chris was there, too.

Freda asked me a lot of questions about my finances and about my assets with the stockbroker. I explained as best I could about the inheritance from my brother, and also told her that my assets would include my car, I think, and my condominium that is paid for, along with some stocks, my checking account and my bank accounts. She listened very intently and said that she felt she could help. Her attorney friend, Gary Bieler, didn't have much to say, but he was also very attentive.

Now I guess before I go on, I must tell you that I've changed the names of these people. I feel it's something important to do, because they have not yet been found guilty.

As the meeting went on, Freda said that she thought she could help me with my dilemma. She had her attorney produce some papers for me to look over and sign, so Chris and I went over them.

Chris said he really didn't understand everything, but he didn't see anything glaringly wrong. Freda and Gary said they have many clients who have similar financial concerns and they help them out in this same way. They also said that these papers would provide for them to care for my finances and me if I would ever become incapacitated. I guess that's ok, because if something would happen to me, I have no one else to see to these matters.

I asked Chris if he would like to oversee my care instead, but he didn't think that would be an appropriate job for him. He said he's not family and wouldn't want to be in a position to possibly have others think he is manipulating me for my money. I appreciate his honesty.

Recently I wrote him into my will as a friend, but after I told him, he asked that I please remove him; so I did. I guess he's serious about just wanting to be my friend and trying to watch out for my needs. I wish I had family that showed such concern....

Well, I signed the papers that Freda and Gary gave to me and they left with all of them. They said that should I ever have a change of heart I could cancel our relationship at any time. All I need to do is let them know and it will be over. That's good to know.

I thought of it after they left: I suppose it wouldn't have been a bad idea to ask them for a copy of what I had signed. But they seem honest, and they did say I could call at any time if I decide I don't want their help anymore.

I've been thinking and rethinking this whole new financial relationship idea. I talked it over some with Chris, too. I really don't think I need anyone to manage my affairs.

As good an idea as it seemed, things have certainly gone well for me for the last 80 years. So, I guess, it wasn't necessary for me to have gotten into this mess in the first place. I pay my bills, I go for walks with Bailie, I have fun with my friends, we go places, and physically I feel as good as ever. What was I thinking anyway? So I'll just call Freda and end this thing.

MARCH 21, '97

HAPPY SPRING

Freda and Gary came over today, and Chris was here, too. Thank goodness for Chris. I explained that, seeing it's only been a couple/three weeks, my real desire is to end our newly formed financial arrangement. I explained to Freda and Gary that I guess I was just overwhelmed with my brother's inheritance, and didn't know what to do at the time. But now that things have settled down, I've had a chance to sort out my thoughts and I can see that I've done well with my affairs up 'til now. And there should be no reason that I can't continue taking care of myself in the future.

Freda and Gary thanked me for having them over. They said they'd be getting back to me real soon regarding all this.

MARCH 30, '97

Took Bailie to the groomer today. She looks so cute when I get her back. The vet had a chance to give her a good going-over and said she's in great health. I said it must be all the walks she takes me on.

The vet asked me if she's good in the car, and I said, "Yes, but sometimes she seems to want to hide under the front seat, and I can't understand why." He laughed, because of the way I kid myself about my driving. I think he's surprised that I still enjoy it so much and continue to pass my license renewals. He said he was happy to see that I get around pretty good for my age, and I said, "What would you expect for 25 . . . (he smiled) would you believe 26 ?"   I don't think he believed 26 either. He said he loves my sense of humor.

Humor or not, I gathered up Bailie, paid at the window and wished everyone well until next time. I think I'll stop for a hamburger on the way home. I know Bailie would like some fries.

APRIL 6, '97

Marion, a lady-friend from nearby, stopped by for a visit. I know my ever-vigilant Bailie, from her nest on the corner of my bed, saw Marion coming, because she started to woof a little bit. Her little bark is so cute.

Bailie enjoys watching out front while she lies on my bed. I have it tight against the wall and right under a window, so she's able to poke her little black nose through the blinds and watch everyone go by. I always know from her little bark that someone is at the door, even before they ring.

Anyway, I was watching the TV news from "my chair" when Bailie woofed, so I started to head for the door knowing she would try to beat me to it. Bailie won, as usual. I say it's "my chair", but Bailie spends more time in it than I do. I keep it covered with a sheet so that "my chair" doesn't get too dirty. I sometimes wonder if I will ever stop chasing dirt. Probably not. I've even got Bailie trained to wait inside the front door after our walks so that I can wipe her feet off; she grumps sometimes when I wipe them. Am I neurotic? Who cares. I know she likes the attention.

Marion just brought over a few little things that I can send out. She always remembers how much I like to gather *stuff* and box it, and send it to unexpecting friends. So she helped me wrap a few things and stayed to visit for a while. Time went so fast that, before either of us knew it, she was staying for a late snack.

It was late when Marion left. But like always before she leaves, she had to give Bailie a big hug and then a kiss on top of her little black nose; and tonight was no exception.

While going out the door, Marion asked me if I canceled my deal with the guardian? I thanked her for reminding me. I haven't heard anything from them for a couple of weeks. I'll call them tomorrow.

APRIL 7, '97

I talked to Freda this morning and she said we should get this whole thing settled soon. I'm glad this is going to work out. The more I keep thinking about it, the more I'm sure I don't need anyone helping me with my money. I would be keeping track of what *they* do with it anyway, so why not spend that time keeping track of what *I* do with it. Maybe, just for fun, I'll bill myself for my services and indulge myself a little with what I pay me--rather than pay Freda and Company.

I think my first order of business might be to get Bailie a new collar. My new job could be so much fun! Gee, come to think of it, I haven't worked since I retired! Now *that's* a revelation! Life has such funny twists and turns. To think I'm 80 years old -- and still employable! Oh, I just make me giggle sometimes....

APRIL 13, '97

Chris and Patricia left for home today. Their real home is along the upper east coast, and they leave about this time of year. I miss them during the summer months, but they usually come back by early-to-mid October. We phone each other often, yet I really look forward to their return. They are both very special to me. I do have other good friends and neighbors, but I really miss them.

Marion and I went to lunch today. I had already gone to the same restaurant for breakfast, but what the heck. It sometimes happens that way, and I won't turn down a chance to go driving somewhere. And the people at the restaurant are used to my being there often anyway.

Before going home we stopped by the bank for a little spending money. I must remember to write that stop down, because I think it was my first fulfilled duty of my new job. Should I get paid once a week or once every other week? Oh, I'll figure that out later.

I took the chance, while going through the bank's drive-through, to "get" Marion a little. Before entering the lane I stopped, gripped the steering wheel real tight, glared straight ahead and cried out "OOOHH, THEY'RE MAKING THESE LANES NARROWER AND NARROWER" and hit the gas. She sat up so straight I thought her head was going through the roof and her foot was going through the floor...must have

thought she had her own brake peddle...
she really stomped down hard. Then she
screamed, "You're crazy!!!" In
German!
We both speak it, but I must have really
got her good, 'cause she didn't realize at all
what she had said.

Oh funny me. You'd think she'd be
used to me by now.

my Bailie

MAY 8, '97

I heard from Freda today. She stopped by this afternoon. She had a bunch of papers from the court...so she finally ended our deal.

But that doesn't seem to be it at all. One of the papers is titled "Petition To Determine Incapacity." She had something else that said we must be in court on July 2nd. I asked her what this all meant. Freda said she believed, being a professional guardian, that I am not capable of taking care of myself properly.

I protested and said, "Everything was fine until you came along." She said my attitude would not help the issue and that a judge would review everything on July 2nd to see if I really needed her help. I didn't know what to say.

Why should some judge be doing all this? I must call Chris. I'm not sure I know what all this means. Freda wouldn't explain anything to me. She just said, "Read the papers and call me with any questions."

This doesn't seem right. Certainly she knows I can take care of myself. Certainly her attorney-friend doesn't know what's happening here. I just hired them to manage my money -- even though I can do it. I'll call her attorney; he should be able to stop her. Chris needs to know. I wish Bailie would pee on her shoes.

Chris was home, thank God! I told him I had a paper here that says it's a petition to determine incapacity. I asked him what that means.

"Read it to me," he said. So I scanned the thing and it identifies me by name and address and it says my "incapacity is based upon the following factual information:"

"The proposed Ward forgets to pay household bills, forgets where the checkbook is, pays condo rent two and three times on occasion, and has no memory of when she last saw a doctor."

And at the bottom I told him that some person named Margaret Doven, R.N., personally observed these facts to be true. I asked Chris who Margaret Doven is? But he could hardly get any words out. "Oh my God!" he screamed. "Do you know what they're trying to do?"

I said "no," and he stumbled through his thoughts. He asked if I remembered that document I signed in February, when we had that meeting with everyone at my house? Of course I remember that. He said that he remembered a clause that said, *should I become incapacitated Freda would be appointed to take care of all my affairs and me.* He blurted out, "They're not going to terminate their contract with you -- they're going to have you declared incapacitated. They're going to try to control your life that way!"

I said, "I can't believe that. You don't really think that could be true, do you?" No, certainly not I thought. I added, "I'll call her attorney, he'll stop this."

But then he asked me, "Whose signatures are on the document?" I looked down and told him it was signed by Gary Bieler and Freda Luelow; the attorney and the guardian. He said, "Forget about calling Bieler, he's probably in on this, too!"

But I asked, "Who is Margaret Doven?" Chris thought out loud again for a moment and questioned, "Wasn't she that lady who sat there and said nothing?"

He was right. That quiet lady was Margaret Doven, (Registered Nurse?) But why did they bring a nurse along? Too many questions not enough answers.

Chris thought out loud again, "Maybe they had this plan in mind all along and needed Doven as a *supposedly* unbiased observer. Unbiased my butt!! I'll bet she's a part of this just as much as Bieler and Luelow," he said.

This is all too much for an old lady. I asked Chris what I should do, what with a court date coming up and all, and he said he didn't know yet. But he said, at the very least, he would have everyone we know attend this hearing to help discredit all their claims.

He said to try and relax (RELAX?) and he would do some checking and get back to me. He said that, if he had to, he would fly down to help.

Bailie must have sensed something was wrong, because while I was on the phone, she jumped into my lap and curled up; and I didn't even know it. Chris said he'd call me back as soon as he knows more.

MAY 9, '97

Didn't get much sleep last night. Bailie stayed curled up with me all the time. Chris called and said he couldn't get a hold of Luelow or Bieler. He'd try again tomorrow, but he did leave a message wanting to know the time for the hearing on July 2nd. He asked me if I could mail him a copy of the petition Freda gave me? I'll certainly mail it to him right away.

I looked over the form again. I wish I understood this petition thing. I got upset thinking that they could lie about claiming I don't pay my household bills, and that I forget where my checkbook is. And that I pay my condo rent two and three times at once?

Chris is our condo president and he knows I've never done that! And, yes, I have no memory of when I last saw a doctor -- BECAUSE I'M IN GOOD HEALTH !

So then I looked a little farther down the page...I hadn't seen this part before. They claim that because I'm incapacitated, I'm "incapable of exercising the following rights:"

"To marry, to contract, to sue and defend lawsuits, to determine residency, to vote, to travel, to have a driver's license, to seek or retain employment, to consent to medical treatment, to personally apply for government benefits, to manage property or to make any gift or disposition of property, to make decisions about social environment or other social aspects of my life."

It's too ridiculous to think I can't do any of those things just because I asked someone for help with my new income. Today is almost over. Maybe tomorrow will be a better day.

I think I'll take Bailie for a nice long walk. We both need some fresh air. "Bailie -- do you want to walk down to the beach?"

MAY 12, '97

Marion and I went for breakfast this morning. Afterwards, when we were driving back to my place, guess who we saw at my front door waiting for my return? Margaret Doven, R.N. I didn't even want to know what she was there for.

So I asked Marion if she wanted to go shopping instead of going straight home? When she said "sure" I quickly turned around in the lot and headed back out. I then explained to Marion who Margaret Doven was.

As we were leaving, I could see Margaret in my rear-view mirror waving her arms frantically and yelling something. This would have been comical, I'm sure, from someone else's perspective...lady running, car leaving. Suddenly, though, I wasn't in the mood for humor.

MAY 13, '97

Freda called this morning and asked why I left Margaret standing at my door yesterday? That question brought a smile to my face.... "It's a free country," I said. "And if Margaret wants to stand at my door all day long, that's her business...."

I guess today was Freda's not-to-be-in-the-mood day. She didn't see any humor in my response. But I was rather impressed with the quickness of my comeback. And at least *I* thought it had a little humor to it.

I guess I had to ask her, so I did. "What did she want anyway?" Freda said that she assigned Margaret to take care of me, because of my "condition." I said I don't have a "condition." But Freda said that my uncooperative attitude wouldn't help me much, and that's why we are going to have this hearing. She said that the court appointed a lawyer to defend me at the hearing. His name is Gerry Gray. I asked who's paying for all this and she said, right now, the court is.

Freda also said that sometime soon I would be receiving an evaluation, ordered by the court, to determine my "condition." And if I had any questions I could call Gray. I called Chris instead.

Chris didn't have anything new to report. He said he got my mail and that he has contacted a bunch of my neighbors. He wants them at the hearing to help me and asked them to also find out the time of the hearing.

Margaret and some other lady were at my door this afternoon, but I didn't let them in. Bailie grumped at the door some, and they probably knew I was home, because my car was outside. Doesn't bother me though, even if they saw me. No law says I have to answer my door.

After they left I went and did a few errands. I hope this all ends soon.

MAY 21, '97

Freda called and said three people would be stopping by today. They are the ones doing this evaluation. She said that I should be home for them seeing that this visit is directed by the court. So when they arrived I let them in. They looked around some, asked me how I was

31

doing -- and left. Really wasn't anything. So much for that.

JUNE 15, '97

Things have quieted down some around here. Margaret has been around a few times, but she soon leaves. The neighbors see her. Sometimes I'm home; sometimes I'm not. Chris and others are still trying to get the time for the court appearance from Freda. She says she will let them know as soon as possible. I would think I'd hear something from *my* lawyer, Gerry Gray, but he hasn't called me.

Chris said he tried calling Gray, but Mr. Gray wouldn't talk with him about the case, because of client confidentiality. I hope Chris can make it to this hearing. For now I just try to forget about all this and go on with things. It should be so easy enough to show the judge that this paperwork is all a pack of lies.

Chris called today and asked if I knew the time of tomorrow's hearing. I said that I didn't know. He said that Freda hadn't called any of my neighbors about it, but that she would call him later today with its time. My neighbors think that Chris doesn't have to come down for this hearing, because they will all be able to tell the judge the same things.

JULY 2, '97

Freda just called. It's 8:30 in the morning. She said that she would be right over to pick me up for the hearing. I asked her if she notified everyone else and she said that's all been taken care of. I hope this goes well.

On the way to the hearing, Freda said that this should be a short matter and it probably won't even be necessary for me to say much of anything to the judge. And, she said, the judge probably won't even have to ask me any questions. She said these things usually go pretty quick, and the judge should have an easy decision concerning our contract.

No one was there except for court employees, the judge, Freda, Gary Bieler, Margaret Doven and a man who introduced himself to me as my lawyer, Attorney Gerry Gray. Everyone was busy shuffling papers and making comments about this being in the file and that being in the file.

That visit Freda arranged on May 21st was called an Examining Committee's Report, and everyone made sure everyone else had a copy of it. Freda said it was just routine. Gary Bieler had said some things about it; Freda said she agreed -- as did Margaret Doven, and before I knew it, it all seemed to be over. Then the judge said something and it was, indeed, all over. I don't even remember that Gerry Gray said much of anything.

Freda took me home and it was still well before lunchtime. I phoned Chris, up north. I asked him why my neighbors hadn't been at the hearing?

He said he couldn't believe it. He told me he talked to Freda yesterday and she said the time had yet to be set, and that she would let me know as soon as possible -- so I could let everyone know. Everyone wanted to attend. He said he couldn't believe she tricked us all like this. She never called anyone.

Chris asked me what had happened, and I said that I wasn't really sure. I said the judge made some kind of decision and I assumed that he terminated the contract. I told Chris that I really didn't understand all the language and legal terms that were flying around, but nobody seemed concerned with the outcome -- so I assumed it went the way I wanted. Chris said he would check into this right away.

I don't know why...I feel a little sick. Chris is too upset....

JULY 9, '97

I received a bunch of mail today from the court, and I don't understand any of it. There's one titled, "Petition To Declare Ward Indigent," and one titled "Examining Committee's Report Following Petition Alleging Incapacity" -- that's the one everyone seemed to make a fuss over at the hearing. Another titled "Letters Of Limited Guardianship Of The Person And Property" and yet another titled "Order Determining Limited Incapacity."

I called Chris right away, but he didn't say much when I told him what I had. He was very quiet. He asked me to mail him copies right away. I said I would. He added that he would call the courthouse to get whatever else is in my file.

I looked over those new papers again, starting with the "Petition To Declare Ward Indigent." I've pretty much determined that I'm the WARD. For some reason, when Freda and Bieler applied for our hearing, they put this paper into the file. It says that I am indigent (without money) and that I have no assets. Why would they say such a thing?

And then Bieler signed a part of this paper saying that he *investigated* and found it to be true that I have no assets -- and that he doesn't expect to be paid for representing Freda. He doesn't expect to be paid? Can you imagine such a thing? I'm beginning to think that I've been their target all along, like Chris thought early on. And that this INDIGENT claim is just to fool the judge into thinking I'm just some poor soul who desperately needs their help. How *HUMANITARIAN* of them all. They found a poor person who needs help...and they'll even work real hard to help me...without pay? I think something's not right.

Don't they remember that it was my stockbroker who called the meeting that took place at *my* house on February 24th? Don't they remember that I have accounts with the stockbroker? Don't they remember that I *own* the house they sat in, and I *own* the car they parked next to? And don't they remember about my wanting their services in the beginning, because of my inheritance? And don't they remember my telling them about my checking and savings accounts? They even said in this "affidavit" that my assets are *unknown* to them. Why would they lie like that? I don't understand. I really don't understand. Why don't they tell the judge the truth?

The Examining Committee's Report says that all my rights should be taken away, too. I remember them being here for only a few minutes! What could have made them make such a claim? It says that I have "Early Senile Dementia." Can that be determined within 3-4 minutes? I didn't take any tests for them! Here's the entire text of the Examining Committee's Report:

EXAMINING COMMITTEE'S REPORT FOLLOWING PETITION ALLEGING INCAPACITY

NAME: Adele Fraulen   AGE: 80
DATE OF BIRTH: 02/03/17

A. The alleged Incapacity is:
The proposed Ward forgets to pay household bills, forgets where the checkbook is, pays condo rent two and three times on occasion, and has no memory of when she last saw a doctor.

B. Based upon the comprehensive exam:

   1. Physical Examination

   a. **Diagnosis:** No records. Has not gone to a doctor for years.

   b. **Prognosis:** Takes no medication. Patient broke leg years ago.

   c. **Recommended Treatment:** None

   2. Mental Health Examination:

   a. **Diagnosis:** Early Senile Dementia.

   b. **Prognosis:** Poor

   c. **Recommended Treatment:** None

   3. Functional Assessment:

   a. **Findings:** Ambulatory - No apparent illness.

   b. **Recommended Treatment:** None

C. Consultation with family physician: No. Has no family doctor and has not seen a physician for years.

D. Assessment of prior clinical history and treatment records, if any: N/A

E. Assessment of any other social records or reports, if any: N/A

F. Factual evaluation of the individual's ability to:

1. MARRY:
- **a. Should right be removed?** Yes
- **b. Factual Basis:** Patient is unable to make informed decisions concerning her welfare.
- **c. Extent of Incapacity:** 100%
- **d. Recommendations for increasing capacity:** None

2. VOTE:
- **a. Should right be removed?** Yes
- **b. Factual Basis:** Patient is unable to make informed decisions concerning her best interest.
- **c. Extent of Incapacity:** 100%
- **d. Recommendations for increasing capacity:** None

3. PERSONALLY APPLY FOR GOVERNMENT BENEFITS:
- **a. Should right be removed?** Yes
- **b. Factual Basis:** Patient is unable to make informed decisions concerning her best interest.

c. **Extent of Incapacity:** 100%

d. **Recommendations for increasing capacity:**
None

4. **HAVE A DRIVER'S LICENSE:**

   a. **Should right be removed:** Yes

   b. **Factual Basis:** Patient is unable to comprehend the laws of operating a motor vehicle and presents a danger to herself and to others.

   c. **Extent of Incapacity:** 100%

   d. **Recommendations for increasing capacity:**
   None

5. **TRAVEL:**

   a. **Should right be removed?** No **Limited?** Yes

   b. **Factual Basis:** Patient should be able to travel as long as she has the supervision of another person to protect her interest.

   c. **Extent of Incapacity:** --

   d. **Recommendations for increasing capacity:**
   Under supervision only.

6. **SEEK OR RETAIN EMPLOYMENT:**

   a. **Should right be removed?** Yes

   b. **Factual Basis:** Patient is an 80 year-old female and is diagnosed with Early Senile Dementia and is unable to retain employment.

   c. **Extent of Incapacity:** 100%

d. Recommendations for increasing capacity:
   None

7. **CONTRACT:**

   a. Should right be removed? Yes

   b. Factual Basis: Patient is unable to understand the complexity of contractual agreements.

   c. Extent of Incapacity: 100%

   d. Recommendations for increasing capacity:
   None

8. **SUE AND BE SUED:**

   a. Should right be removed? Yes

   b. Factual Basis: Patient is unable to comprehend the complexity of laws as they pertain to her.

   c. Extent of Incapacity: 100%

   d. Recommendations for increasing capacity:
   None

9. **MANAGE PROPERTY OR TO MAKE ANY GIFT OR DISPOSITION OF PROPERTY:**

   a. Should right be removed? Yes

   b. Factual Basis: Patient is unable to balance checkbook. Patient either does not pay or over pays her bills.

   c. Extent of Incapacity: 100%

   d. Recommendations for increasing capacity:
   None

10. DETERMINE RESIDENCE:

a. **Should right be removed?** No Limited? Yes

b. **Factual Basis:** Patient is able to determine residence under the supervision of someone else.

c. **Extent of Incapacity:** 90%

d. **Recommendations for increasing capacity:** None

11. CONSENT TO MEDICAL AND MENTAL HEALTH TREATMENT:

a. **Should right be removed?** Yes

b. **Factual Basis:** Patient is unable to determine her physical and mental needs. She has not seen a physician in years.

c. **Extent of Incapacity:** 100%

d. **Recommendations for increasing capacity:** None

12. MAKE DECISIONS ABOUT SOCIAL ENVIRONMENT OR OTHER SOCIAL ASPECTS OF LIFE:

a. **Should right be removed?** No Limited? Yes

b. **Factual Basis:** Patient is able to make decisions about social environment under the supervision of someone else.

c. **Extent of Incapacity:** 90%

d. Recommendations for increasing capacity:
None

G. DETERMINATION:

THE examining committee has examined the alleged incapacitated person and recommends the following:

The scope of guardianship services needed is limited. The alleged incapacitated person should retain all rights except those specifically set out hereinabove in F.

We have spoken at length with F. Luelow, M. Doven and Mr. Almund (brother) and our evaluation is based on information provided by them, in addition to an individual home visit with Mrs. Fraulen.

Signatures: 05/27/97

Joseph Winters, M.D.

Mary D. Dumphy, MS, LMHC

Laurie Mettinger, MSW, LCSW

There is also a letter attached to this report signed by Dumphy and Mettinger. It's simply a letter to the court confirming their findings, and the last line of their letter says:

"It is believed that Ms. Fraulen can be easily victimized in light of her mental impairments."

Is that what this is all about? Have they found me to be a *victim* they can all easily exploit? I must be reading this wrong. Maybe Attorney Gray can straighten this out.

I called Gerry Gray, but he wasn't in to take my call. I left a message for him to call me regarding Freda Luelow. The secretary asked if this is concerning work he does *for* her or if this is a case he was appointed to represent *against* her. You mean he does both? She said "sure."

I think I need some help.

I still haven't heard from Attorney Gray, but Chris called me. And Margaret has been hanging around like the Grim Reaper, too. Usually she is alone, but sometimes there is someone else with her. I told Margaret that I don't want her around, I don't need her help and that she is wasting her time. I won't let her into my house.

Chris said he called Gray's office and Gray answered the phone. He told Gray he was calling about my case, but Chris said that Gray stated he didn't recall it. Their conversation was pretty short, he said. Chris said that he would try to contact a local attorney to straighten this out. And he would be calling state agencies to enlist the same type of help.

Chris knows that everything Luelow and Bieler claim against me is intentionally false, and that it may take some time to get it straight. He said he tried speaking to the judge, but that the judge won't talk to him "ex parte" (other side not present). So much for that, he said.

But he'll keep trying to enlist help wherever he can.

I told Chris I don't like having to avoid Margaret the way I do, because I shouldn't have to feel like I can't come and go as I please. I know this mess upsets him very much and that he seems to feel responsible. He feels that he should have realized early on that something wasn't right. I feel bad for him. I know he has my best interests at heart and really shouldn't be involved in this at all, except that I asked him for help.

I'll let Margaret come and go as she pleases. I asked Chris if we could, maybe, get some kind of court order to keep her away. But he thought that what she actually has, through Freda, is a court order to *be* my care-taker. So how could we keep her away without reversing the judge's decision? I don't know, but he said he'd check into all this.

And about Gray working *for* and *against* Freda? Chris filed a complaint with the state's Bar Association, but they said Gray's conduct was ok....

JULY 26, '97

Got more mail from the courthouse. This one is titled, "Petition To Terminate Ward's Insolvency." Apparently it looks like Freda is claiming she found enough of my money to pay a bunch of fees and court costs? Somehow she has control over my money now?

There are some receipts attached that show that I paid Freda $363.00, Bieler $1505.00, Gray $600.00 and the Examining Committee $650.00. I paid for all these lies? Chris will be disgusted to know that Gray remembered me enough to at least bill me. I don't know how much more of this I can deal with.

One of the receipts shows a billing record to me from Freda listing her hours. It starts with 2.2 hours on February 24th for an "Initial Visit To Assess." That was the first meeting we all had. Then there are 22 other entries for time spent between February 24th and yesterday.

But then there's something dated May 8 where she claims, under oath, answering "NO" to a question:

"At the present time, is the applicant (Freda), or applicant's business, corporation or other business entity, providing professional, personal or business services to the incapacitated person?"

And to this she answers NO? Then why am I paying her from February 24th? Seems like business to me! She better not be billing me to be my friend!!

You know, I'm not too smart about professional business dealings, and I never cared to be. But at least I know how to keep track of money, and I learned good how to add and subtract. When I'm paying someone for something, to me, that's what I would call a Business Service. She's a liar, plain and simple!

Probably figured no one would ever notice.

There were also many requests from Freda to the judge asking for more time to submit a full list of the "Ward's Assets." I guess there is still nothing in front of the judge to show him I have all kinds of money, except for Freda's recent claim of finding just enough to cover fees and costs.

Chris said he asked Freda how she could justify having submitted all those bills for payment, and she said, "They must be ok, because the court approved them all." Let's see if I get this right: She's saying that, "I will submit *any* fabrication, lie, falsehood, scam, deceit, criminal activity...and if the court doesn't catch on, then my submissions are automatically legitimate." She'll blame the court when her submissions are wrong, because after all, if her submissions aren't absolutely legal, the court won't approve them? This is entirely the court's fault? They should tell me when I'm not telling the truth?

It's hard for me to comprehend the criminal mind. She's not stupid; probably just amazingly arrogant -- and she may be getting some pretty creative legal advice from Bieler on how to abuse the system. I'm sure that advice comes with a price tag, which is probably "a piece of the action ($)." I wonder how much he's really making on all this?

She's so caught up in greed she's not remembering that, when caught, she'll probably be the one left to swing all alone. Suddenly, she'll find her lawyer doesn't seem to know her anymore: "Freda? I don't seem to remember a Freda...." Ask Attorney Gray, he's good at that excuse.

Why isn't anyone paying attention to all this? She's not afraid of lying to the court either. At this point I wouldn't believe Freda if she *told* me she was lying.

I hope I'm not getting numb to all of this. Time to take Bailie for a walk. Maybe I won't come back....

They got me in the parking lot today. Margaret and some lady from an in-home care agency were waiting, and I didn't see them right off. Too late by the time I noticed.

This other lady said that her agency was appointed by Luelow's Guardianship Agency to see to my care. I said I didn't need anyone appointed to my care. She stated that if I continued to refuse, she would have to report that fact which would not look good on my record. I'M SUPPOSED TO CARE ABOUT MY RECORD? I said, "This whole thing is a farce and I don't care what you report to who" -- or is it whom....

Chris has been calling state agencies and new attorneys trying to get all this reversed. He said he's had no luck with the state. And when he calls attorneys he finds that they are not interested. One even yelled at him to not bother with any of this -- that he'd just be wasting his time. Chris found out later that this guy was, at one time, in partnership with Bieler. He's also learned that Bieler's father is a U.S. Congressman. Why am I not surprised?

I got a notice from the bank the other day that Freda and Company has taken court-ordered control of my financial assets. They run the show and I get an allowance. I can't even hire an attorney to sue her. I, according to the judge's order, lost my rights:

"To contract, to sue and defend lawsuits, to personally apply for government benefits, to manage property or to make any gift or disposition of property, to have a driver's license, to marry, to seek or retain employment, or to consent to medical treatment."

No one has said anything about turning over my driver's license yet, so I continue to motor on. The judge says I have limited control over:

"Travel, to determine residence, to make decisions about social environment or other social aspects of life."

It seems like they'll let me choose my friends. Guess who's not even on the long list?

SEPTEMBER 07, '97

Chris and Patricia are back today. It's so good to see them again. I always feel a little empty when they go back up north in the spring. But when they return in the fall, it's like having a family reunion. I'm so lucky to consider them my family. Chris said he's already made appointments with some new attorneys, and he hopes one of them can help me.

SEPTEMBER 12, '97

My neighbors watch this dance between Margaret and the nurse lady and I. They come over, I ignore them, they leave. They come over, I ignore them, they leave. This goes on all the time and it's getting to be a perverted game.

Sometimes they try to talk with me while I walk Bailie. I try to get her to bite them, but she's too nice to do that. Maybe Bailie needs a friend...like a pit bull. Then maybe they'd leave me walk alone.

So we're sort of in this holding pattern that may go on forever. They keep telling me I can't drive without a valid license. I say, "Don't worry, it's just like fishing without a license; the fish bite just as well." They don't laugh. Boy, these two must have no fun. I figure if I *don't* make a game of all this, it *will* drive me crazy.

I know I'm paying for their time, but for now there's nothing I can do about it. Maybe it's good I do have my brother's inheritance to pay for all this, but then....

My hope is that Chris will be able to get this all straight. For now I get my allowance, and there's nothing more I can do. They own all my rights. I sometimes go to sleep at night wondering what country I'm really in. This doesn't seem like free America anymore. The Luelows and the Bielers probably wouldn't agree. I'm sure they think everything's just fine.

Bailie and I went for a long walk. No one tagged along. She's such a good girl.

SEPTEMBER 15, '97

Among Chris's many duties as condo president, and caring for the sickness in his family, he still finds time to help me. I don't know how he does it all -- and I wouldn't be able to do it myself.
Remember, I don't have any rights.

Chris has seen a number of new attorneys, some not in this area, and they all say this is going to be very expensive to un-do. Chris doesn't have a retainer of $1500; plus what it may cost to win or lose. There are no guarantees. I'm really stuck, I guess. But Chris isn't giving up.

My neighbors are friendly, but they don't understand what's going on like Chris does. They see me coming and going, but don't realize what's really happening. I know they have their own lives and problems to deal with. Thank

God for Chris. I wish I could pay him for his time.

NOVEMBER 8, '97

I don't want to write these words, it's really hard. Please God; help me. Bailie; where's BAILIE! I need to hold her.... Oh my, I was just at the restaurant having lunch as usual. Oh Lord, this is terrible. I was having lunch and I noticed this tow truck pulling into the lot. It stopped for a moment. I didn't pay any more attention to it as it went around the corner. A few minutes later it came back around and it was towing *MY CAR*. I tried going out after it -- but... *FREDA* was in the doorway. She handed me a piece of paper that said, IMPOUND ORDER. It was from the court. She said she was there to take me home. She says, it says, my driving is a *threat to the community*.

My car is gone. My *LAST* freedom is gone. All I can do is cry. "Bailie come, I need you."

Chris and Patricia haven't been home for a few days. I know they have friends in a different part of the state. They usually don't go away long. I hate to have to share the latest with them. I didn't get any sleep last night. I just kept shaking. Bailie was a big help to me. We went for a long late-night walk. She's the only thing I really care about. I love my dog.

The Witch (Margaret) and the other lady came over this morning with groceries. I'll call it a Care Package for the Prisoner. What's left for me to do except have them bring it in. It hurt me so to have them enter my house. I didn't say anything to them -- I probably paid for the groceries anyway, and they left quickly.

I suspect their routine will be to slowly have me *adjust* to their presence -- sort of like training an animal. What can I do, sue them? Call the police? Take them to court? No, none of the above. I could run away from home, but then I don't have any money either. I think I'm a little old to become a run-away.... An 80 year old run-away and her dog.... What a sight that would be.... Frankly, Bailie deserves a better life than that. If that's true, what about me, Freda? Or should I be asking Gary Bieler? Or the Witch? Who's listening, except Chris.

NOVEMBER 27, '97

Happy Thanksgiving. At least I still have my friends, and my life...and my health. I spent the day with Chris and Patricia. They are just like family. Chris has been sending out letters to whoever (whomever?) he thinks might be able to help. So far he has had no luck. But he keeps trying. I pray that we are able to someday get this behind us. He and Patricia need to spend time taking care of their own lives.

DECEMBER 3, '97

Time to get going on Christmas cards. I have a bunch to send out. The Witch and the other lady (I don't care to know her name) said they'd take me shopping for cards. But I wouldn't want to be seen dead with them. I'm convinced that I am only their meal-ticket. They have no concern for me.

So I went out with Chris, and it was a nice enough day to take Bailie, too. She loves to ride in the car. Gee, I don't even know where mine is.

We got some nice cards and a roll of stamps. I send out quite a few, probably 50 or more. "You've gotta send 'em to get 'em," and I like receiving them, too. It helps me feel like I'm able to share the holidays with others when, for the most part, I'm pretty much alone. I do send Bailie a card. She likes ones with kitties. I'm sending her one with a lion!

That's too funny....

Anyway, I'll start writing some out tomorrow. Sounds like a plan.

I'm almost done with my cards. I should finish up in a couple of days. I like to write little notes, and that takes time. And it's hard to find something good to say -- do I tell them about what's really going on here? Maybe I should. But then, I'm not sure anyone would believe me.

In today's mail there was something else from the court. It was titled "Ward's Inventory Of Assets." Apparently Freda and Company finally found out what I'm worth and submitted it to the court. Who cares anymore.

I think if they told the judge what my assets were prior to the hearing, the judge would have maybe gotten wise to their actions. Now, some clerk-aide probably just filed this away and the judge will never see it. I'll bet that all the other papers where Freda and Company lied were filed the same way. Just some clerk to see that the required *papers* are in, *not caring* what they actually *say*. The judge would have to be *blind* otherwise not to see what they've submitted. Oh well....

Freda just called.   Said she has something she wants to show me.   She said Bailie could come along, too.

The remaining pages of Adele's home diary were found to be empty.

JERILANE ASSISTED LIVING CENTER

March 12, 1998

Mr. Jack Carerra

Freeman Services, Inc.

Social Services Department

Dear Mr. Carerra:

This fax was requested by you to follow up on our telephone conversation this morning. My name is Chris Zurillo and my hope is that you will be able to interview Ms. Adele Fraulen and document her situation. As an outside observer, I also hope that your report will assist me in getting the help of others to free Adele.

As I discussed with you, Adele Fraulen came into an inheritance that she felt she could not handle. I believe the professionals she hired to assist her have gone beyond their authority and have gained complete control of her life.

They have forced her into a locked nursing home against her will and probably did this without court knowledge or approval. She is in an adjacent county and state law requires a court notice when a "Ward" is placed anywhere outside of her county of residence. There is no court notice in Adele's court record.

After returning from a short vacation on December 13th, my wife and I noticed that Adele's house lights were not on after dark. She never goes anywhere after dark, so her lights would be on if she was home. We checked with neighbors and they had not seen her either. We checked inside her home and could not find her or her dog.

I phoned her guardian, Mrs. Freda Luelow, who said that Adele was taken to a nursing home, because she was unable to care for herself. She said that Adele has become belligerent lately and refused to accept any professional care. She said her car was in storage, but she would not tell me where Adele was or where her car was.

Freda said that Adele needed time to adjust to her new home, and that no one would be allowed to see her for at least a few weeks. I finally had a chance to see Adele two weeks ago and the place she is in is intolerable. It smells like a toilet and she has no personal freedoms. She shares a small room with another person and she has no closets for her clothes. They are piled on a chair. The only bathroom is down the hall, and everyone shares it.

Adele said that her roommate needs her diapers changed constantly and the smell is terrible. No one from the staff does it, and to make the smell go away Adele changes them for this lady. Adele said they need changing several times a day and she mostly does it.

Last week my wife and I took Adele out to lunch and apparently we didn't get permission. I didn't know that permission was necessary. When I brought her back there was a big fuss by Margaret Doven who said that I would not be allowed to do this again and that, as punishment, I would not be allowed to see Adele for two weeks. Who was being punished?

The only thing Adele wants is to go home. That's all she keeps asking for every time we talk to her by phone. She also wants to know where her dog Bailie is. This is a very sad situation.

I have been talking with Adele's brother's nurse who knows of the Jerilane facility and also knows some of its nurses. She says that Adele is under the care of a psychiatrist by the name of Christopher Jaconis. Dr. Jaconis is prescribing a medication called HALDOL® to Adele and this nurse does not think this is at all necessary.

She has given me literature on HALDOL that I am sure you are aware of:

A. It is not recommended for older adults, because they are especially sensitive to its harmful anticholinergic effects, and it is not to be used unless absolutely necessary. It is an antipsychotic drug with sedative effects.

B. It can cause confusion, delirium, short-term memory problems, disorientation, impaired attention, body tremors and/or Parkinson-like symptoms. These symptoms may take 3-4 months to clear after stopping this medication. These side effects are potentially irreversible and have the highest prevalence in the elderly -- particularly women.

C. It is indicated for treatment of severe hyperexcitable behavior that is not provoked.

HALDOL is apparently designed to control dementia and should not be administered to those without dementia, because its side effects in normal individuals can give the appearance of one having dementia. Its use on Adele, being a normal elderly woman, appears highly questionable. Unless they are trying to CREATE in her an appearance of dementia?

Her brother's nurse also says that Christopher Jaconis is part corporate owner of Jerilane. Is it right for the owner to also be the patient's doctor -- who is also the patient's prescribing physician? When Adele is "in session" with him as her psychiatrist, how much attention will her pleas for freedom really get? This seems like the fox owning the hen house! I cannot help but wonder how many patients there are, like Adele, in this place under Dr. Jaconis's care? And are they there just for the sake of Jaconis and his corporation making a nice profit? Being her brother's nurse, she knows Adele and does not think Adele should even be at Jerilane, and that HALDOL could be a dangerous drug for Adele to be taking.

This nurse asked me how Adele's walking is, and I said that she's walking slower and not picking her feet up well. The nurse called this side effect the "HALDOL Shuffle." Apparently this is an insider-joke to those knowing what HALDOL can do to some people. I asked Adele if she was taking any pills and she said no, but apparently this medicine can be mixed with foods like applesauce and pudding. Adele says there is always some of that with her meals.

The few times my wife and I have been allowed to see Adele, we are not permitted to give her any reading material and we are checked to see that we do not give her anything else. Someone, usually Margaret Doven, is there to listen to our conversations from the time we arrive until the time we leave. I do not know about our phone calls, but I would not be surprised to know that they might be monitored, too.

Mr. Carerra, I hope you can help with your evaluation of all this. I think it is an ugly and intolerable situation that no one cares to look into. I have tried to get the help of all government agencies that have been recommended to me without any luck. My efforts for the last many months have become concentrated since Adele disappeared on 12/12.

I have called or written every Federal, State and local government and private agency recommended to me. My contacts have ranged from the FBI to the local eldercare hotline. I cannot begin to recite all the excuses given to me for the lack of anyone's help, but they include the FBI saying this is a private matter, the ACLU saying they are simply not interested, the State Attorney saying this is not a criminal matter, to the local elder hotline saying this is a criminal matter out of their jurisdiction. I have nearly lost count of the private attorneys I have sought out. Adele does not know of all my efforts to gain her freedom; I fear my lack of results would be too disheartening for her.

I have several different court documents that I can give you for your review, but unfortunately the documents that started this whole problem are not available. I made a terrible mistake by not reminding Adele to get copies of everything she signed the first day Freda Luelow and Freda's attorney were at her home, and they will not send me copies. Lacking those documents has made my attempts to free Adele even more difficult, because I cannot show how this all began.

I need your help and look forward to meeting you. My hope is that any report you can supply me will eventually interest someone. I am not giving up on trying to get Adele free.

Sincerely yours,

Chris Zurillo

FREEMAN CONSULTING SERVICES

CONSULTANTS TO THE HEALTH CARE INDUSTRY

EVALUATION - Private Consult

Date: March 13, 1998

Requested By: Mr. Chris Zurillo

RE: Ms. Adele Fraulen

Mr. Chris Zurillo contacted this office requesting a professional evaluation of the status of Ms. Adele Fraulen. He reports that Ms. Fraulen is an elderly, single woman essentially in the midst of having her assets embezzled by her legal guardian and others. He states that she is presently institutionalized and being provided with assisted-living care. Mr. Zurillo was advised that this office performs confidential consulting services to help improve the quality of public and private health care facilities and does not provide the type of evaluation he is requesting.

However, because of the perceived serious nature of Ms. Fraulen's situation, and his reported exhaustive efforts to gain assistance from all proper authorities, this office is willing to provide this evaluation.

His desire is simply to have this report (if supportive of his theory) document this case and use it to seek further assistance toward resolution. Mr. Zurillo is aware that this office is not an enforcement agency.

FINDINGS

On this date my wife and I met Mr. Chris and Mrs. Patricia Zurillo at Jerilane Assisted Living Center at 12:15PM. Mr. Zurillo was already in a heated discussion with a woman introduced to me as Ms. Margaret Doven. Ms. Doven is reportedly Adele Fraulen's guardian and works for Ms. Freda Luelow (as mentioned in the file). The Zurillos introduced us to Ms. Doven as "old friends" without further explanation.

Mr. Zurillo is quite upset with the "imprisonment of Adele against her will," as he was expressing to Ms. Doven. Ms. Doven stated to me that whenever Adele is with the Zurillos she is upset for some time after. Ms. Doven was not going to allow any of us to see Adele, but Chris persisted, so she agreed to allow us to go in with Patricia only. Mr. Zurillo had to remain outside.

It appears likely that Mr. and Mrs. Zurillo will, in the future, not be allowed by Ms. Doven to see Adele. Ms. Doven impressed me as not being protective of Adele, but defensive of the association with her.

When we met Adele she was dressed neatly and she appeared to be normally groomed. The meeting was orchestrated in the main living area and Ms. Doven was (hopefully) just out of listening range. Adele wanted to know if we were there to take her home. We greeted her in a manner consistent with being "old friends" and answered to the effect that we would like to help if we could.

This common living area was furnished with living room style furniture and all pieces were covered in heavy plastic slipcovers. The room had other "residents" sitting about, and the room smelled heavily of urine.

I began to quietly ask Adele questions related to the facts as reported by Mr. Zurillo. She had no trouble recalling events from the distant past (including where she was originally from), how long she had been in this state, where she had lived and for how long, the circumstances surrounding her confinement and other events of life. I purposely changed from distant past, to present, and in between as frequently as possible, and she had no trouble keeping up with her recall. At first she appeared lethargic and uninvolved, but her interest increased as she talked about herself and her situation. I suspect she also began to understand the real purpose of our presence. She made it very clear that she is able to care for her hygiene, as she always has, and simply wants to go back to her home. She asked me if I knew where her dog Bailie was. I answered, "No, but Chris is working on that, too. "

From a practical and legal standpoint she does not understand how she became placed against her will in this facility. She understands that it all started when she was looking for help with her finances. Adele stated that she does not need, want to be at, or continue to stay at Jerilane.

At times she would cry a little, but she would regain herself and continue. Adele is very aware of her good financial condition and stated that she believes she has been confined to Jerilane so that her money can be controlled, and eventually taken from her.

At this point Ms. Doven stepped into the conversation and stated, "You people don't seem to be who you say you are, why are you here?" Ms. Doven continued to question our relationship to Adele, but we stuck with the "story" and she eventually dropped it.

The only potential memory recall defect that came up was whether or not Adele had lunch today. Adele said she had, and Ms. Doven said she had not. Ms. Doven whispered to me that this is the type of problem they have to deal with concerning Adele. And then she said to Adele; "Adele you didn't have lunch today - don't you remember?" Adele, by body language, shrugged Ms. Doven off and let the subject drop. Frequently Ms. Doven would bring up some event to Adele and ask, "... don't you remember Adele?" This statement seemed to be for our benefit as Ms. Doven took opportunities to suggest a failing Adele.

I talked to Ms. Doven aside for a short time and she stated that Adele's condition really requires her to be in a secure facility. And she expressed concern that outside visitors are not doing Adele any good. I asked what she meant by "good" and Ms. Doven stated that outside visitors just leave Adele with confusion and a longing to go home.

I asked Ms. Doven if Adele has Alzheimer's Disease and she stated that Adele did not; but that she has "some kind" of dementia. Ms. Doven stated that when they "found" Adele at her home, the home was a mess inside, it was unkept and there was "absolutely no food in the house." She added that it was a terrible sight, and that Adele is now much better off.

We then left Jerilane Center and went with the Zurillos to Adele's home within a condominium complex. When we walked in, it was as though a very tidy person had been abruptly removed from their home during normal daily activity. A number of observations were very striking:

Immediately upon entering, a living room chair was draped with a clean white knit sweater, and a small rag was inside the door--to the left. Mr. Zurillo stated that every time (winter) Adele took her dog for a walk she would wear the sweater, leave it on the chair for the next time, and wipe off her dog's feet.

Another chair across the living room had a cloth covering the seat. Next to the chair was a TV tray containing some papers and a TV remote. The seat cloth was slightly askew as if someone had just been sitting in the chair.

The inside of the refrigerator (some foods could now stand to be discarded) was neatly arranged with a modest amount of items, as was the freezer. It was in no way empty. The kitchen dinette table contained Christmas cards that Mr. Zurillo stated Adele was in the process of completing the last time he saw her. He stated that Adele did her own grocery shopping and, almost daily, went to a local restaurant for lunch. Several employees know her there.

Adele's bedroom was believed to be toward the front of the home. Her bed had an impression in it where the dog appeared to lay and look out the window. The window blind was slightly raised in one spot where the dog probably looked out.

Adele's inside laundry room was completely in order and neatly arranged. Appropriate items were on shelves above the washer and dryer. Throughout the home, nothing was found to be in an unusual place indicating that someone living there was not in his or her right mind. The home was clean, appeared handy for its occupant, orderly and well under the control of its resident. The bathrooms were clean and in good order. The condo layout was; two bedrooms, two baths, living room, kitchen/dinette and outer enclosed sunroom.

The furnishings were tasteful, and most furniture was covered and/or had fitted plastic covers (probably, because of the dog). Everything had a place and appeared to be in its place. This was all in sharp contrast to the condition described by Ms. Doven. The home has been vacant for approximately 12 weeks and had no detectable odor.

OBSERVATIONS

From simply the standpoint of Adele's condo, there was no reason to believe that she did not have full control of her surroundings. It appeared that Adele used the smaller of the two bedrooms for her use along with the second bath. The main bath had a few small boxes that appeared to be in the process of being packed with small knick-knack items. Mr. Zurillo advised that from time-to-time Adele would pack such boxes to give away to people. This particular project seemed to have been interrupted.

I CANNOT CONFIRM MS. DOVEN'S STATEMENT OF ADELE'S DEMENTED

It would seem unlikely that Adele's friends would clean her home to make it presentable. As an example, I observed that, next to the front door, below a front window, there was a potted ivy plant in an 8-inch deep pot. It appeared stressed from lack of water. I drove my fingers through the dirt to the bottom of the pot. All levels of dirt were completely dry. This would be expected for a plant that has not been watered for about 12 weeks. If neighbors and friends were covertly cleaning Adele's condo I suspect someone would have, even unconsciously, watered the ivy.

It is more understandable for neighbors to seek help for someone living in poor conditions rather than clean up and then try to get the neighbor back home. It would seem more likely that Ms. Doven, et al., is deceptive, potentially for financial gain as claimed by Mr. Zurillo and suspected by Adele.

As an observer of human behavior, I detected no deception on the part of the Zurillos or Adele. Ms. Doven, in contrast, is very defensive and appears on the brink of not allowing any outside contact to Adele. Ms. Doven claims her interest in Adele is not one of money, but I suspect she "protests too much." I personally doubt that Ms. Doven, Ms. Luelow and Mr. Bieler would show such intense interest for Adele had they met her as homeless, penniless and living on a street corner. In fact, Mr. Zurillo's claim of this bordering on false imprisonment for money may be closer to the truth. All professionals now in Adele's life, including Jerilane, are being paid to care for Adele directly out of Adele's own assets until those assets are gone.

CONCLUSIONS

Adele appears to be a typical 81 year-old in control of herself. Her state of initial lethargy and disinterest could easily be due to her unwanted confinement, our unusual presence, and continual suggestions by Ms. Doven that her memory is failing.

I found no such memory failure in the brief time Adele and I talked. Ms. Doven made a pretty big deal about Adele's recall of lunch, but my impression of Adele's response was that it was not anything to make a big deal about. I would tend to agree with Adele, considering *Ms. Doven* might even be deceptive.

There does appear to be a financial motive for Luelow and Bieler to have moved as quickly as they did to remove Adele from her home. They first came into Adele's life in February, served her with a summons for guardianship in May, and had her removed from her home in December. Her car and driver's license were taken away from her even though she reportedly had a clean driving record and drove almost daily.

It should also be noted that Adele's claim that she does not belong in a lockdown facility could be seen as dementia by itself. It is generally assumed that someone *in* confinement *requires* confinement. Their claim to the contrary further tends to make "normal people" not want to listen to them, **because** of where they are. After all, it's easily assumed that their pleading to be let out "just goes to show they're crazy."

In retrospect, I would fear to be in Adele's position; because the more of a scene I would make to be let out, the more I would be seen as demented and in need of help. After all, "I'm already committed to an institution and therefore deemed to be unstable -- as Ms. Doven clearly tells everyone." Unfortunately, many people throughout history have been led to their death after innocently accepting their fate.

Mr. Zurillo stated that he has contacted the attorney appointed to represent Adele against Luelow and Bieler and stated that the attorney had no recall of the case. Luelow and Bieler also reportedly hid the hearing time from concerned neighbors wanting to defend Adele.

Adele appears quiet-spoken and believes what she is told. It would be likely that she would have a limited concept of legal matters and strictly sought help, originally, for her financial matters. She is very aware that something got way out-of-hand.

Mr. and Mrs. Zurillo appear to be motivated by the 11-year friendship they have had with their neighbor Adele and a desire to correct an injustice. Additionally, Mr. Zurillo was the first one Adele came to for help with her finances and he advised her to seek a professional. He stated he briefly went over the papers Luelow and Bieler asked her to sign, and advised her that he did not see anything wrong with them. He now feels guilty about telling her that and probably feels responsible, to some degree, for the position she is in. Now, because of his outbursts with Ms. Doven, Mr.

Zurillo appears close to being an unwelcome guest at Jerilane.

Regardless of Adele's present condition, the initial act of confinement appears fraudulent, with the possibility of fabricated evidence presented for judicial consideration. It is scary, yet in this case likely, that someone, without family to fight for her, has been removed from society for the financial gain of others.

I made two suggestions to Mr. Zurillo as we left Adele's condominium:
1) Go ahead and water the ivy plant.
2) Seeing that entrance doors are condo association property, consider changing Adele's locks.

I suspect that as/if Mr. Zurillo succeeds in gaining Adele's freedom, her guardian may try to sell the property so that Adele would not have a home to return home to. The guardian could then claim that Adele is better off where she is, because she has no other home.

Further, I suggested that no one should be allowed into Adele's condo without a court order. If a court order should be presented I suggested, under suspicion the document could be fraudulent, that entry still be denied until a uniformed Sheriff is present to enforce it. The Sheriff's presence would go toward authenticating the court document and allowing another delay to determine any new course of action.

Thank you for the opportunity to perform this very challenging evaluation.

Respectfully submitted,

Jack Carerra
Consultant/Social Services

CHAPTER 7. CHRIS TO THE RESCUE

MARCH 18, '98

I found a note in my dress pocket this afternoon after Chris and Patricia left. It says, "Don't eat the applesauce or pudding -- it has a bad drug in it." I wonder if I really care. Everything is so depressing around here. I'll give him a note back thanking him -- I suppose that's how I should give him real news. Seems like the only way to do it -- we're always watched like prisoners.

Most of the time I don't care to say anything to anybody anyway. But I will pass him this note when I see them tomorrow. I'll just give him a big hug, slip my hand into his back pocket and whisper in his ear to get my note. And I'll put some of my own thoughts down -- he can keep my diary notes. Then I don't have to hide them around here. I miss writing my diary. I miss driving my car. I miss my home. I miss my dog. I miss, I miss, I miss.... When will this all end.

Chris, please help me.

MARCH 20, '98

I've been mixing my applesauce and pudding in with the other trash I don't eat. No one watches. The sauce and pudding were all I usually ate anyway, so with *all* the trash mixed together my plate really looks the same. Maybe the reason I'm feeling a little better lately is because of not eating those things. Unfortunately I think I see things a little more clearly around here. *Was that bad drug supposed to help me cope with imprisonment?*

It seems like I've been here forever -- entombed. There's no place to go. The Witch takes me out to the store every now-and-then, but I have no money to buy anything with. She buys some things, probably with my money, too! I don't always feel well, but maybe the smell of human excrement will cause that. This place is called Jerilane Hill, but it's really a Pit. I fed Bailie better food, and everybody sits around here and pees in their pants. I can't stand it. Oh, I miss her.

When I first came to this Pit -- it's no fun to remember -- Freda tricked me into going with her. We drove up along a stony driveway and passed a cheap sign that read "Jerilane Hill Assisted Living Center." She said she wanted to show me this home. I wanted to jump out of the car and run.

This place is an old, dark-brown wood-sided ranch style house. The front is dumpy and stretches out for an unusually long distance. It may have been someone's home at one time and has probably been added on to. The lot is heavily wooded, and from the back of the house the lot slopes away to a pond, leaving the home's lower-level rear exposed. Sort of a bi-level, but you wouldn't know it from the front.

We left Bailie in the car and Freda walked me up a long ramp to the front door. It was locked. She knocked, the door buzzed and she pulled it open. We went inside. The door closed behind us with the sound of a metal jail cell. It was locked again. Are we visiting or just looking? Must be just looking I thought, I brought nothing with me. I told Freda I didn't like it. Didn't like it at all.

The front door opened onto a large living room. A dining room with living room furniture was to the far right and an eat-in kitchen to the far left -- sort of around the corner. The living room/dining room had all its furniture covered in fitted plastic. There were old people sitting around everywhere, some were eating in the kitchen, and the place smelled like urine.

Freda walked me through/between the living rooms down a dark and empty hallway. The hallway had four bedrooms, two on each side. Each room had two beds. Those rooms didn't smell any better either. At the end of the hall was the bathroom. I didn't even want to see it.

Freda took me back into the first bedroom on the right. Nothing special. Two beds, a couple of chairs, no closet. Freda said, "Make yourself at home" and left.

My poor Bailie was still in her car.

Chris got my note the other day. He said so in one he gave back to me. I found it in my dress pocket again. He said, "Keep writing to me." So every time they visit I'll make sure to give one of them a big hug and slip my paper to them. We can't talk much about anything, because the Witch, or someone else who reports to her, is always hovering around while we talk. So at least this way I can pass them a note and they can pass me one. They keep theirs small, so I can flush it down the toilet when I'm done with it. I'm acting like I'm in jail. Before long I'll probably be eating them and swallowing them. I suppose that would be better than the food here.

Chris wrote that he had someone here a couple of weeks ago, if I remembered the visit. The man has written a report on his visit with me and Chris hopes that his letter will help me.

I remember that visit and I *thought* Chris was up to something, but I didn't care to make the effort to put it all together. What would I do without the both of them? Patricia gives me moral support while Chris fights for me. What a wonderful team.

I pretty much keep to myself around here and just wait for the day I get to go home. This doctor I see here seems to have no use for my asking to go home. He probably hears that from everyone here. I can't believe what's going on. Yet I have no choice but to be patient. I don't see Freda anymore, just the Witch.

APRIL 1, '98

Chris and Patricia took me OUT to lunch today. We weren't alone though, the Witch had to come along. So much for talking about anything important. I'm so glad we got this note thing going on. I'm able to keep up my diary, and Chris or Patricia can give me news.

Chris doesn't get to come in that much anymore. I always can hear him yelling at the Witch in the parking lot, so I know when they have arrived. And she always goes out there to meet them. I know they have to always make an appointment to come see me. I must have so much to do....

The note Chris gave me today said that he called the TV station about my problems, and he says that they are going to look into this. All Patricia said is that Chris is SO happy. I remember that he could not get anyone to listen. I hope this works out. I'm still staying away from the sauce and pudding.

APRIL 2, '98

Chris said in today's note that he found an attorney to help him. The attorney understands that I cannot hire him, because I've lost the right to do that. But maybe Bob can? I wrote back to go ahead and call Bob. The problem is that this attorney wants $1500 for a retainer.

Bob's got that kind of money, so I said get it from him, and tell him I'll pay him back when I'm out. Oh my God, it sounds like I'm up for parole or something....

APRIL 4, '98

Chris phoned today and said Bob would go ahead if I would put Bobby Jr. in my will as sole beneficiary. I completely understand. Tell Bob to *TAKE A LEAP !* So how's that for family. I started to cry and couldn't stop. Chris said he'd call back in a little while.

LATER - APRIL 4 PM

Patricia called back and we talked some about my brother. I really didn't care to talk much about it. Chris came on the line after a while and said that he'd come up with the money and that I should not worry about it for even a minute. It's so sad, I've got the cash to pay it, but there is no way I can get to it. I'll pay him back even though he says he won't take the money. I would die in here without them. Or would they keep me alive just enough to bleed me dry. I think there *was* something in the food. I'm really beginning to see things much more clearly than before.

The moaning and crying that comes up from downstairs is unnerving. There are about 17 of us in this house, and maybe half live in the lower level. We up here don't see them. They are said to be bedridden and in need of special care. So we never see them, we just hear them. This place is really The Pit.

APRIL 6, '98

Very interesting day today. Chris and Patricia brought Marion to visit and the Witch let her in. But she hung around like the Grim Reaper as usual. We were all greeting each other when, suddenly, Marion said "Adele, hören Sie auf mich." She's speaking to me in German!!! ("Adele, listen to me.") She continued in German; "Don't mind my sing-song voice, I've got something to tell you and I want your nurse to think I'm just asking you how you are. So every now and then say something like ' I'm fine, how are you, or whatever'. Verstehen Sie ?"

("Do you understand?")

... Come on -- I don't believe this!!! This is just like out of the movies -- Chris really dreamed up a good one this time....
So I said, "Yes, I'm fine. How are you?"

Marion continued, in German;
"The new attorney wants a signed paper from you saying that you want to get out of here and go back home. I have it with me, so I want you to give me a big hug and I'll put it in your pocket. Then go to the bathroom and sign it and get it back to me before we leave. Verstehen Sie ?"
I said, " THANK YOU !!! "

This is almost too much fun. There was a pen with the piece of paper and we talked a while before I "had" to go to the bathroom. The paper said, "I, Adele Fraulen, want my rights restored and to be returned to my home and to have my dog Bailie returned to me." I came back, probably smiling too much, and gave Marion a big hug and dropped the paper in her pocket. The Witch never saw a thing. Too busy shining her broom.

We all laughed and hugged and it was probably quite a sight. But this is a good day. Chris said out loud that his money problems are solved, too. How glorious!

APRIL 20, '98

Chris didn't hide it this time. He trooped briskly past the Witch and handed me a stack of papers. She wanted to see what they were first, but Chris told her she could get her own copies from the courthouse. The Witch stepped back and said nothing. WOW !

Chris told me that our new attorney filed these new papers with the court asking that I be released. The paper that Marion had me sign was also a part of this. There's even a court date set for July 15th with a new judge! And my new attorney will have another attorney, appointed by the court, working with him, too. Chris said the court was specifically asked that this appointed attorney be sought from outside this area, and have absolutely no ties with Luelow or Bieler. Chris said that I'd also be getting another evaluation soon.

He made sure that the Witch heard all this, too, because she'll be calling those two as soon as her blood stops boiling. ...She's starting to look like a tomato.

Here's some of what he gave me:

IN THE CIRCUIT COURT FOR
(COUNTY, STATE)
PROBATE DIVISION

IN RE: THE GUARDIANSHIP OF
    Adele FRAULEN   File No. 9707805CP
_____/ Division: J

SUGGESTION OF CAPACITY

    Petitioner, Chris ZURILLO, files this Suggestion of Capacity and represents that:

1. Adele Fraulen was adjudicated incapacitated by the Circuit Court of (this) County on July 2, 1997.

2. Petitioner's interest is as follows: Friend and neighbor.

3. The Ward is currently capable of exercising the following rights which were removed:

    To contract, to sue and defend lawsuits; to apply for government benefits; to manage property or to make any gift or disposition of property; to consent to medical and mental health treatment; limited to travel; to determine residence; to make decisions about social environment or other social aspects of life.

4. A notice requesting restoration signed by the Ward is attached.

    Petitioner requests that the Court inquire into the capacity of the Ward and, if the Ward is found to have regained capacity and is capable of exercising rights which have been removed, that the Court enter an Order of Restoration of Capacity restoring all or some of the rights which were removed from the Ward.

    Under penalties of perjury, I declare that I have read the foregoing and the facts alleged are true to the best of my knowledge and belief.

Signed on April 20, 1998.   ChrisZurillo,
                                    Petitioner

There was also this letter from Chris:

4/20/98

Judge Carl Vilance
Circuit Court for (this) County
Probate Division
File #97-07805 CP

Dear Judge Vilance:

We are concerned about the current health care of our neighbor Adele Fraulen who is a subject of Guardianship before this court. Adele is being treated with a drug called Haldol. As you can see from the enclosed documents this is not a drug for older persons. It tends to worsen the situation.

We can see no reason that Adele should not be returned to her home. We feel that with a bank trust officer managing her financial affairs and a home health care person visiting her that she would be fine. The Guardian is getting ready to sell her car and may be considering selling her home. This kind of action would only tend to hasten Adele's demise.

Adele calls us every day to find out how we are progressing in getting her home again. If we could personally tell this story to you we believe you would understand that a grave injustice has been done to Adele Fraulen.

It would be greatly appreciated if the court would look into this matter at the earliest possible time before she falls through the cracks.

Respectfully yours,

Chris W. Zurillo
Patricia B. Zurillo

He said try to be patient. He thinks things might start to get a little nasty, what with everyone trying to hide what's been

going on and all. I hope this all works out. I can hold on.

We hugged and laughed a little and then Chris had to leave. He said there was a lot to do yet. On the way out he told the Witch: "You better be good to her and clean her up, she'll be out in public soon. And you probably don't want her looking like the abuse she's been receiving here, do you? Adele, how 'bout lunch tomorrow? Margaret's treat! Maybe something other than applesauce or pudding, hey Margaret? We've got to put some meat back on her bones!"

The Witch just stood there with her mouth open.

NOW she's heading for the phone.

APRIL 24, '98

Chris and Patricia came by again today. It was their second visit. Chris said they would be back after they went to the courthouse. This time back, Chris showed me some papers he said Jack Carrera drew up for me. Chris said he signed it all and gave it to the court earlier today -- to help out the papers the new attorney submitted.

It's all a little complicated, but the attorney's papers don't really tell the judge my history, so Mr. Carrera and Chris thought something should be in the court record giving all the details. This way, the judge has something to really look at.

Mr. Carrera said -- don't worry if this is not a completely proper thing to do, because being "submitted" by Chris as a concerned citizen, the judge will probably allow its entry into my record. He said if an attorney did this, it might not be allowed. So Chris proudly showed it to me and said I could keep it. I think it's a good idea to tell the judge just what's been going on.

I think it's also important to show all these legal papers, because they might just help someone. So, this is what Chris sent:

APRIL 24, 1998

Judge Carl Vilance
Circuit Court
Sixth District
      RE: Adele Fraulen   File #97-07805CP

Dear Judge Vilance:

      I have petitioned this court to reconsider restoration of capacity to the Ward in the case listed above. The petition was delivered to your court on 4/20/98. There may be some irregular circumstances to be aware of concerning the acquisition of this Ward by the guardian and her attorney.

      Please use any concerns expressed here as grounds for your own motion to investigate potential irregularities in the way this Ward was eventually confined. My abilities to look into these concerns are limited and my understanding of their legal meanings may be in error. I have taken great care to present these circumstances as they present themselves; and I personally am making no legal claims of wrongdoing on the part of any parties involved. I have information to believe that:

1. The Ward came to me in 02/97 for advice on how to handle her new income from her one-half of the earned interest on a nearly one

million dollar trust willed to her by a recently deceased brother. The trust itself is then to be willed to a college upon the death of the Ward and her surviving brother.

2. I advised the Ward to seek professional help, so she contacted her stockbroker.

3. The stockbroker arranged for the guardian (of record) and the guardian's attorney (of record) to meet with the Ward at her home.

4. The guardian and her attorney presented the Ward with a revocable financial management agreement.

5. The Ward signed the agreement, but within 2-3 weeks met the guardian and her attorney, again at her home, and expressed her desire to cancel it.

6. This cancellation request was not honored. The guardian and her attorney then filed a petition to the court on 5/8/97 seeking full guardianship of this person.

7. *The guardian and her attorney further petitioned to the court on 5/8 that, after investigating, they believe their Ward to be INDIGENT, having no assets, or her assets are unknown or unattainable; this being 73 days after hiring them to manage her assets; income from the $1 Million trust.*

8. History of the case file shows three extension-of-time requests by the guardian to file Ward's Inventory Of Assets with the court.

9. *Under the penalty of perjury, the guardian further tells the court on 5/8/97 that she has no business relationship with the prospective Ward.*

10. *Guardian's billing record filed with the court shows continuous billings to the prospective Ward as her business client since 2/24/97 and through 5/8/97. According to this same record, the guardian had first contact with her attorney regarding this prospective Ward on 2/27.*

11. The attorney's billing record on file with the court shows his first contact with the guardian to be on 4/3/97.

12. Hearing held on 7/2/97; limited guardianship granted. No Inventory Of Assets yet filed.

13. 7/13-23: Guardian's court billing record shows her having contacts with Ward's asset holders (stockbroker, banks, mutual fund holders); this being 11 days after the hearing. The guardian's previous 73 days of investigation found no assets. See #7 above.

14. 12/97; the guardian submits Ward's Inventory Of Assets to the court.

15. Any Inventory Of Assets received by a court, especially well after a hearing, may normally

not come to the judge's attention, but would simply be filed into the court record by an aide or clerk.

16. 12/97; the guardian removes Ward from her home and confines Ward to Jerilane Assisted Living Center.

17. Jerilane's corporate records list a corporate owner as being one CHRISTOPHER JACONIS. A Dr. Christopher Jaconis is said to be prescribing a medication to the Ward known as Haldol. Haldol may have serious side effects when prescribed to normally healthy, elderly women. Haldol may present a previously normal individual as one who now appears incapacitated.

    The Ward was living well and doing well on her own before connecting with the guardian and her attorney. She operated her own automobile that had no damage, and is thought to have a clear driving record.

18. Upon the guardian's petition to the court, the Ward's driving privileges and driver's license were taken away and her car was impounded; said to be a driving threat to the county as a whole.

19. In the guardian's initial petition claiming proof of incapacity, the Ward was said to have paid

her condominium fees unnecessarily several times.

I am president of her condominium association, and this never happened.

By having a lengthy delay to the introduction of a Ward's Inventory Of Assets, especially until well after a case has been closed, such a delay may prevent a presiding judge from investigating the motives of petitioners against a prospective Ward: Particularly a prospective Ward who may be financially desirable.

As an Addendum to item #19 above, and in regard to the guardian's initial claim of Ward's Incapacity, the petitioner (guardian) lists four points of incapacity. She and her attorney present these four points as cause for such a finding:

1. The proposed Ward   forgets to pay household bills.
2. The proposed Ward   forgets where her checkbook is.
3. The proposed Ward   pays condo fees two and three times on occasion.
4. The proposed Ward   has no memory of when she last saw a doctor.

Upon checking the court records supplied by the guardian and her attorney, I found no supporting evidence to substantiate (#1) nonpayment of household bills, (#2) lost checkbook or (#3) over-payment of condo fees.

Contrary to #1. I checked with the Electric Utility Company about Adele's account history prior to her being removed from her home in 12/97. Maintaining this utility could be considered life threatening should its service become interrupted. Their records show her to have been a customer with a *"good credit history for the previous two (2) years, has had no disconnects and has had no late-payment notices sent."* Her water bill, an additional life threatening service, was paid from her condo fees.

I have personal knowledge that she has not had her phone disconnected for any late payments nor has her car or home insurance been canceled for any late or non-payments. Her condominium did not have a mortgage. I am aware that from time-to-time Adele made mail order purchases and paid those bills when due.

Contrary to #2. The routine and timely payments of all these bills would indicate someone who has had no trouble locating their personal checkbook.

Contrary to #3. As president of her condominium association I am personally aware that she did not over-pay her monthly condo fees, and they were paid on time.

Contrary to #4. **The doctor from the court-ordered Examining Committee reported Adele to be in good physical health; having not seen a doctor for years, is taking no medication, and is ambulatory with no apparent illnesses.**

It could be normal for a person not seeing a doctor to have limited or no recall of the last time a doctor was seen.

There are only **THREE WORDS** *in all these court records that allude to the claims of the guardian and her attorney. These words are* **EARLY SENILE DEMENTIA;** *and they are found in the Examining Committee's report concerning Adele's Mental Health Examination after the one visit to her at home.*

Unless I missed seeing it, I could find NO evidence such as medical reports, functional assessments or psychiatric evaluations substantiating those three words. Those **THREE WORDS** *have been used to severely alter this Ward's previously free style of living.*

I remain concerned about the report that Haldol is being prescribed to Adele, and I have

learned that there is an expression in the nursing home industry -- "The Haldol Shuffle." This is apparently because Haldol makes a person walk in a shuffling way and appear to be in a depressed and lethargic state that would be contrary to their normal condition. I know that Adele would want to present her best to you, but may be incapable, because of Haldol.

Respectfully yours,

Chris Zurillo

I guess I really had no idea of what all these goings-on has meant until I read this. It's pretty clear that I've been in trouble for quite a while. I think that Mr. Carerra and Chris have done a good thing. At least this information is now part of my court record and can't be twisted, as some later verbal testimony might become. They think this letter will really help in the end. I sure hope so.

I saw another doctor today. He is the one Chris said would be doing a new evaluation. Not much to report though. He just asked me a few questions, looked around a little and left.

Suddenly, I'm a little afraid for all the waves we've been making around here. This place is really in a state of upset. No one seems to know what's happening. We have new employees, because some of the old ones just left. This morning a man from down the hall was found dead out back. Everyone's wondering how he got out of this jail. He's been some trouble for the staff, just like me I guess, and they say he drowned in the swamp. Face down in a couple feet of water. The police said it was an accidental drowning.

There's been talk that the state is going to close this place down, too. Chris said that the real owner is a convicted felon, and that his name on the business license is a fake. Because of the conviction he's not allowed to own a place like this. I just want to get out of here alive -- and before this place gets closed. Chris is afraid I'd get shipped to who-knows-where.

MAY 16, '98

Chris had some news today.
He said that the condo office told him an appraiser was at my house today trying to get in, but couldn't. Chris said that he had the lock changed some time ago. So the appraiser then went to the condo office to see why his key wouldn't work, and the office said, "Because your key won't work." They gave the man no help. Chris seemed pretty proud of himself.

The appraiser asked for some help to get in, but the office said that, "No one is getting in without a court order -- so says our president. Come back another time." Chris said he was warned they might try to sell my home. He's done a good job of stopping them. He also explained his plan "B" should they come back again.

He said it's hard to believe that Freda and Company would really try to sell my house right out from under me; and do it without court permission. But why would that be anything new? He explained that the best thing to do is to try to stop them, every way possible, from selling my home. I can see his point that if I do not have a home to go back to, then I might just have to stay here or somewhere else under the Witch's care.

Chris said that he would let me know if they have to go to plan "B", but that for now the court will find out what they're attempting, which should make them stop. He added that, even if they try to come back, there is also a plan "C". But he doesn't know yet what that might be. He's working on it. He's so funny sometimes.

So, if it weren't for Chris, my home would be sold and I wouldn't even know about it. Chris said that he and Patricia want to get this all straightened out before they go back up north. Imagine where I would be without their help.

He also said this new evaluation report confirms that I should stay where I am. He's livid. But, in the end, he thinks this report might just help us. This doctor says I'm on a medication called ZOLOFT®. News to me. THE MASHED POTATOES !   What's left to eat ?

Chris says ZOLOFT is an antidepressant, but the doctor says I'm "perfectly happy" with my situation. So Chris is thinking, "He says she is on an antidepressant -- does he care to figure out why?   What might she be depressed about?   But then, if she is depressed -- and needs ZOLOFT, is she truly PERFECTLY HAPPY? Which is it doc: Is she Depressed or Perfectly Happy ?"

All these people must work together for a common evil. This doctor also says that I told him I don't like Chris and that I believe the only thing he's after is my money. I never said such a thing!

Chris says we should try this doctor out on HALDOL, or ZOLOFT, or maybe combine them and see how *he* does. But Chris said maybe this guy is already *perfectly happy.* I like his sense of humor when he's upset. Even on days that look a little dim.

JUNE 3, '98

Chris and Patricia said we're going someplace new for lunch today. The Witch doesn't watch us anymore while we are all together here, and she hasn't bothered coming with us when we go out. Chris said when we get to the restaurant we are going to meet some people from the TV station, and they want to do an interview. I guess that's why Patricia asked me to put on my best today. This is all getting so interesting.

I met the newsman I've been watching for years. His name is Scott Anderson and he's been the TV station's investigative reporter for as long as I can remember. He was with his partner Brian, and Glen, their cameraman. They were all so nice, and we even had some time to joke around a little. Scott's demeanor in person is even more impressive than on TV. I was so very glad to talk with them, but they had me tell them everything about what's been going on. Sometimes I'd just as soon forget. But we all went over everything and I was glad that Chris and Patricia were there, too.

Scott said that they've been doing a lot of work on this case so far and credit Chris and Patricia with keeping it going. He said it's been a very complicated story that started with a phone call to them from Chris, followed by the report from Jack Carerra. Scott added that Mr. Carerra's report was something he was not able to put down once he started reading it. He said that Chris gave them all his files, including all the court records -- and Chris's recent letter to the judge was already in there and getting everyone's attention. Scott said that with all that information they hope to help publicly expose this scam.

They were very glad to have finally met me in person and we all got along well. I got a little nervous when Scott said he wanted to get some of our interview on videotape. He thought I would do real well though. He was really encouraging. So we started going over the story from the beginning.

I explained how and where I grew up, and some things that went on with my career and personal life. Scott turned out to be a great kidder. Even the film man, Glen, seemed to have fun. But then we got into this serious stuff and I started to cry. Scott and Brian were very kind and helped me get back on track.

They knew all about Jerilane, but I told them a few things they didn't know. Brian asked me how I could live in such a place; I told him that I didn't have much choice. We talked about the first meeting I had with Luelow and Bieler, and how they turned against me so quickly. We talked about Bailie -- and I started to cry again. I asked Scott if he knew where Bailie was and he said YES ! Oh, I couldn't believe it. He said that Bailie was with Jerilane's manager and was doing ok. I asked Scott if he thought I was going to be able to go home and get Bailie back. He said he would try his hardest. Then he started to cry a little.

After everyone got recomposed, we continued the interview, did a little more film, and then it was time to go. Scott, Brian and Glen offered to take me back so that we could spend that extra time together. I said that would be nice. So we drove around some, talked a little more about my troubles, and headed back to Jerilane. I didn't want to leave them. I felt very protected being with them. They know about life, they know about problems. To think I've watched them on TV all these years and now I'm with them.

We sat out front for a while. I don't think they wanted me to leave and go back inside. I opened the door to leave and Brian started to tear up. Then I did again. But prison awaits. Scott gave me a hug and said, "We'll see you again soon." I sure hope so.

I went inside. The door slammed and locked. This was quite a day.

JUNE 17, '98

I must say, the staff here has been pretty nice lately. Not so much the Witch though. She leaves me alone, but she's not very happy. But then, I guess, she never has been.

I talked to Chris today and there's even more news: The new attorneys have issued subpoenas to EVERYONE connected with Freda and Company. They are going to take depositions from everybody before our new court date.

Chris says, but doesn't want to get my hopes up, that this could be the "beginning of the end." He has uncovered so much through all this that he thinks they are pretty much stuck, having dug their own graves. Probably thought no one would notice, but someone did!

Chris also told me that the court ordered Bieler to respond to that April 24th letter Chris sent to the judge (the one that outlined all the events and lies created by Luelow and Bieler). According to Chris, my new attorneys say that Bieler's answers are "unresponsive and do not substantially dispute Chris's claims."

Chris was so glad the judge not only saw his letter, but also acted on it. He thinks their end is near, because the letter finally exposes, in writing and public record, what has been going on here.

Chris loves the idea of depositions, because we can learn a lot from Freda and Company being forced to answer all kinds of questions. And now we can compare any new answers to their old documents.

Then Chris showed me an interesting little study he did a while back. He said he went backwards through state corporation records starting with Jerilane. He wanted to see if there might be any links that would take him from Jerilane back to Luelow or Bieler, or anyone else connected with Freda and Company.

From Jerilane's records, he found one of its corporate owners to be my doctor here (Jaconis), along with some woman with the same last name as the man who is the convict (hidden owner). Apparently the convict tried hiding his ownership of this Pit by using the name of a woman.

Then, these two owners of Jerilane, and Jerilane's own corporate attorney, are associated with another attorney who represents a retail store. This retail store sells wall coverings. This wall-coverings attorney is associated with the owners of a home-based travel agency -- that is next door to a home-based, non-profit social club. A corporate officer of this social club is a business partner with a law firm. The law firm is Bieler's father. And the attorney who yelled at Chris that, "he is wasting his time trying to get me free," was once a law partner with Bieler's father, *and* a business partner with Bieler's mother.

This may not go far toward proving very much, but it sure is interesting to even end up with any type of connection. Chris said he really didn't expect to find *anything* from this records search, but he seems to think there *could be* a trail of association leading from Bieler, through his father, directly to Jerilane.

At the very least, Chris now understands why this one attorney took the time to yell at him about me being confined by Luelow and Bieler. Chris said this guy's mood changed as soon as Chris mentioned the name Bieler and, at the time, he couldn't understand why. It is unfortunate, I think, that this attorney didn't explain to Chris that maybe he shouldn't express an opinion about my case, because of his dealings/friendship with the Bielers. Instead he pretended to render a thoughtful opinion about by case.

Chris said it did make him stop to think that maybe he *was* wasting his time; but, in fact, this attorney seemed to enter this fraud by hiding his association with the Bielers -- by insinuating there was nothing wrong with my story.

Wouldn't it have been easier to just say, "Sorry, I know Bieler and I think any opinion I may express about this case could be seen as biased." *But no, protect your buddy, and yourself (who knows if somewhere HE is involved in all this) -- just go ahead and add to my misery.* I suppose many attorneys must work very hard to deserve the bad reputation their profession has earned.

Look at how many lawyers have involved themselves in my case, (I don't mean ARE involved, I mean HAVE involved). First, there's Bieler. Then comes the judge (he's an attorney, too). Then the judge appoints another attorney to represent me the first time I'm in court. This one was to *fight against* Bieler. But it doesn't stop there. Chris has to find another attorney to try and un-do what Attorney Bieler and Attorney Judge have done. And, if that's not enough, Attorney Judge appoints yet another attorney to help represent me once Chris's attorney gets this all opened up.

So far I count 5 attorneys; and my situation isn't over yet. I think they all help perpetuate work for themselves, whether they represent one side or the other. And if one of them makes a mistake...well, that's just another reason to create work ($$$) for even more attorneys (friends). It doesn't end. They won't allow it to end.

One contrary note to all this though: When Luelow and Bieler took away all my rights, they also took away my right to hire my own attorney. That doesn't make too much sense if they all try to create work for one another, unless Bieler and Luelow didn't want me to expose what they were up to. Then it would be in *their* best that I am not able to hire anyone to help me out; similar to what the "yelling" attorney tried to accomplish with Chris.

I was told that I couldn't even approach the court on my own -- because I had that right taken by them also. I think

Luelow and Bieler are trying really hard to get away with all this, but they didn't take Chris under serious consideration. They probably didn't remember that there will almost always be a "Chris" hanging around somewhere. Or they forgot: *S o m e d a y -- you WILL be accountable.* And yes, I know, I've done some editorializing here. Forgive me please, but at my age -- I think it's ok....

Anyway, Chris doesn't think that Freda and Company will want to subject themselves to depositions. And, again, without getting my hopes up, he thinks that this will all be over even before the court date. Does that mean I'll be going home soon?

"Just sit tight," he said.

JUNE 26, '98

We all went to lunch again today. Sure wish I could buy. Even Scott came along. He just said he wanted to know how I was doing. I said I was ok. "Am I going home soon," I asked ?

"Just sit tight," he said.

JUNE 30, '98

The court date has been postponed ... until August 24th. What's going to happen until then? Chris said, "Don't worry, I think it's a good sign. It was Freda and Bieler who wanted the postponement." He thinks they are trying hard to avoid this deposition thing. I sure hope so.

Chris likes my new court-appointed attorney. He can bill me just like Gerry Gray did, but this guy is apparently so enraged by all this that he is going to help me for free. Chris is not able to really talk to him directly, but he said that having this other one on retainer is his link to him. The attorney he hired is the one who submitted all the right paperwork that has gotten this all reopened. I hope I can give them both a big hug when this is all over.

CHRIS AND PATRICIA ARE HERE, THEY SAID

PACK MY BAGS, I'M GOING HOME !!!!!!

I DON'T BELIEVE IT-- THIS CAN'T BE TRUE --
THIS CAN'T BE HAPPENING

Chris, don't fool with me like this.   Pack ?   I have no bags ....let's just GO !

This isn't real; please tell me it's real! Chris says it's real. They gave up! The court date will just be a formality! No more fighting, no more arguing, they just said, "Take her home, we won't protest." It's in writing - - - let's go!   This is too much for an old lady to bear...BUT I LOVE IT !

I walked out the door, ran out the door, and didn't look back. I heard it lock behind me for the very last time. I'M FREE!

Patricia took my clothes and there's nothing more I want from that place. I told her not to take anything *they* bought for me. I don't want it in MY house. That sounds great -- MY house. Let's go; let's get out of here before someone changes their mind. Can I drive? Oh, I don't care. Let's just go. I can't wait to see MY house...a 10-minute drive. I can't believe this, finally!

Oh. This is so beautiful. All my neighbors are out and they put ribbons and bunting and *stuff* all around the place. A big banner says, "Welcome Home Adele." I'm gonna cry. Scott is here with Glen and Brian and they are interviewing and filming everything that moves. Not too often I get to cry and laugh at the same time. THIS IS THE BEST DAY OF MY LIFE !

Everyone is hugging and laughing. Chris gave me a big hug and said that he didn't even put anything in my pockets this time. Glen is crying again, too, so he had to stop filming. He was fighting back his tears and trying to tell me that this is the best story he's ever covered. Poor man could hardly talk as we both hung on to each other. Scott wiped a few tears from my eyes with his necktie. Then I saw his eyes start to get red, too.

There is so much chatter and carrying on -- and I don't want to miss a thing. It is soooo good to see everybody and I haven't even been inside my house yet.

I saw Glen reach for his camera and swing it around toward my front door. More people were streaming out and everybody started greeting each other all over again. And crying all over again.

I can't speak ... this is too much for an old lady; but I'm loving every minute of it. There's food and banners and good friends -- this is a real party. What can I do to make sure this isn't some kind of dream...maybe I'll know when I wake up tomorrow in my VERY OWN BED.

No one left for a very long time. The sun went down and many friends were still around. Slowly, slowly the crowd thinned out. But I didn't want any of them to leave. I know it's getting late, but this is a day that's not supposed to end. Yet you don't know how much I'm looking forward to sleeping in my own bed.

I quietly asked Chris, later in the evening, if anyone has seen Bailie. Sure would be nice to have her with me tonight, too. He said, "One thing at a time, people are still working on that. I know it's a lot to ask to wait a little, but it should all work out."

I'm so grateful for everything that's been done for me I was afraid to ask him about her. But he understood perfectly well, because Bailie has been as much a concern for him as I have been. Dear Chris and Patricia. Who could ask for better friends? And neighbors.

...The crowd has left, the house is quiet, except for a nurse. It's almost the atmosphere of Christmas. Rita said she would be staying with me for a while; just to make sure I'm able to settle in ok. She said this was part of the agreement to get me home -- and it makes good sense. I would like having someone around for a while. It would be too strange to come home after all this and not have someone around. Once I have Bailie here, then I'll have all the companionship I need.

Rita made me a snack and I said, "Good Night." Now it's off to sleep in my very own bed. I never thought I'd see it again. I wish Bailie were here to enjoy this with me.

AUGUST 6, '98

BAILIE !

Scott, Brian and Glen and another whole bunch of neighbors are at my door. I couldn't help it: I fell to the ground; my heart is in heaven...she ran to me and jumped in my lap kissing me all over my face. They freed her, she's home now, too! This is all too good to be true, again! I can't stop crying like a baby. Everyone is just watching and taking a moment to gather around me and be my friends. She is so beautiful! Marion reached over and gave her a big hug and kiss right on the nose -- like always! My life is now complete!

I'm paying so much attention to my baby -- I'm not being a very good hostess. I thanked and thanked and hugged everyone, especially Scott. I hope everyone stays all night again. With all my attention being on my dear Bailie, I had to ask my neighbor Phil not to be too jealous. He said he'd get over it. Rita went to get dog food. Another great day. They're really adding up.

Scott and I had a chance to talk some after things quieted down. He said he wanted to bring me up to date on a few things about Bailie -- off the record. He just thought I should know.

He said that they had a hard time finding her after the day I got home. Even though part of the deal for me coming home was for me to adjust first, they still kept an eye on Bailie's whereabouts. Scott said that, for the longest time, she was with Jerilane's manager. Then Bailie was passed on to their daughter's house, but

Bailie didn't get along with their children. So Bailie came back to the manager.

After I came home, according to information Scott was able to gather, Freda ordered that Bailie be removed from the manager's home and hidden. He said that's when they lost track of her even though they had been watching the manager's house. The manager denied knowing anything about my dog. But after my story aired, the manager's neighbors and family wouldn't buy that story and they forced the manager to retrieve Bailie and turn her over. I said I couldn't believe Freda would do that; but my experience with her proves otherwise. Scott said he was just glad to have Bailie back home with me, and that I should watch the news later, because they plan to show this whole reunion.

Scott also told me another interesting story from just today. He said that Freda called my new court-appointed attorney with a fabrication designed to get me back into a nursing home. As the story goes:

Freda told him that, according to Rita, I "had a terrible night last night and was agitated and restless and not adjusting well, was very uncooperative and might have to go back to a care facility." So the attorney talked to Rita who said, "No, Adele is doing fine, I'm the one who had a terrible night and was restless and couldn't sleep. A patient of mine that I stop to see, during some free time I have away from Adele, tried to stab me the other day and I just couldn't get comfortable at Adele's." So Scott said it appears Freda and Company will try anything to save themselves.

Scott also said, if I didn't know it already, that Luelow had filed a complaint with the State's Attorney against Chris accusing him of seeking control of my assets. He said Chris was put through a very intensive criminal investigation as a result of that complaint, but that he was eventually cleared of the allegation. I said I hadn't been told this. Poor Chris, he's been through so much. But Scott said that Chris took that chance to turn the investigation back onto Freda and

Company. Leave it to Chris not to miss an opportunity.

Anyway, life is getting back to normal. Bailie will be with me tonight. "Bailie? Want to go for a walk? We'll go down to the beach, ok?" She wags her tail.... She is *such* a good girl.

AUGUST 10, '98

The state closed Jerilane today. I got out of there just in time. Still can't believe I'm home.

AUGUST 15, '98

Scott came by this afternoon. He is so full of news. I guess that's why he's called a newsman? Not much of a joke, but at least it's an effort....

He said that there was a court hearing held a while back and they would be showing it on the news tonight. Scott said the hearing was because Luelow and

Bieler were not willing to release their control of me.

Apparently my two new attorneys were trying to negotiate with Freda and Company to let me go, but they hadn't been having much luck. So the two of them had asked the judge for an Emergency Hearing. Scott said it was quite fascinating and it went something like this:

Freda testified that Mr. Zurillo's only reason for wanting me back home was to get my money, and she (Freda) should remain my guardian to protect me. The judge told her, "Anything about that is in the past and I don't care." Scott said that Freda just kept it up with that accusation and finally the judge yelled, "*Shut up about it already*" -- and then the lawyer Chris hired (one of my two boys) jumped up and objected to the slanderous statements Freda was making about his client -- Chris. Scott said, with the yelling and all, it was quite a scene.

Then Scott said the hearing turned toward my Bailie -- this is the other side of the story about her return to me. Scott said that my new court-appointed attorney (the other one of my boys) was trying, for a long time and with no result, to get Freda to reveal where Bailie was.

So, having no luck outside of this hearing, he asked her about Bailie under oath. Freda answered that, "It may not be in my client's best interest to have her dog returned if she has to be removed back to a nursing facility." *Then the judge took over.* He asked, "Isn't it supposed to be in your best interest to keep Adele at home? Are you helping her or helping yourself ? *Where is the dog?*" Then Freda answered, "Well, I don't think it would be fair to the dog to bring it back into Adele's life if only to have it taken away again." To which the judge yelled, "WHO'S YOUR CLIENT, THE DOG OR ADELE ?" But Freda kept avoiding the question of "where's the dog" -- so the judge forcefully and harshly asked Freda, "*Is the dog available or not ?*" And finally Freda answered, "yes." So now I know...the rest of Bailie's story.

But Scott said, "This story isn't over yet." He said then came the question of my two boys wanting Freda and Company officially removed from my life. Scott said Freda had the nerve (or stupidity) to ask the judge, "If you would like, I can recommend a friend of mine to replace me," but the judge yelled back, "*Absolutely Not! I'll appoint your temporary replacement without any help from you.*" Then Freda resigned as my guardian before the judge could have the pleasure of judicially removing her.

Oh yes, Scott had one other observation from this hearing. He said that Freda's attorney, Mr. Bieler, wasn't there to represent her. She showed up alone. Could it be that Bieler didn't want to answer a whole bunch of questions either? Isn't it funny how rats run when the lights comes on.

Then Scott gave me a doctor's letter addressed to the judge. It was a letter from that doctor who stopped to see me at Jerilane -- for that re-evaluation. Oh, it's so hard to even write that name, *Jerilane*.

Anyway, this was from the doctor who "examined me" and said I was Perfectly Happy to be at the Pit. Well, after Chris made some of this doctor's discrepancies known to the judge (through the boys), the judge asked him to clarify his position. So this doctor wrote to the judge, "When I examined Ms. Fraulen the possibility of going home was not addressed. She did say that she missed her dog and wished she could be with her. I understand from her court-appointed attorney that Ms. Fraulen has returned home with supervision. I think this is a very plausible solution."
Nice back-peddle doc! I've got to show this to Chris.

Scott added one last bit of news. He said that he and Chris were asked by the judge to meet him privately after this recent hearing. Scott said the judge indicated in a roundabout sort of way that he was sorry all this had happened to me and thanked the station for staying with my story.

But, primarily, the judge wanted to personally thank Chris for submitting that April 24th letter to him about my trouble. The judge said it had become a very important document to him, because it was the only thing he saw in my file, having nothing from the first judge, that clearly outlined what had gone wrong here. The judge said without that letter addressed to him personally, he probably would not have been so well informed on what was wrong -- and it allowed him to take personal action to help solve all this. The judge said that the letter would go a long way toward helping as the court's investigation of Freda and Company continued.

So Scott said, "Watch tonight's news. If you have the stomach for it."

It's just a beautiful summer day. Chris and Patricia took me out to lunch and they went with Bailie and me for a walk. It seemed like we all let out great sighs of relief every now and then.

My other neighbors and I get together, too, and it's just like old times. Seems funny to say that; old times. Old times were just 8 months ago; it feels like a lifetime. But I try to think of it as if "I'm just starting over." Or like I'm getting better after a really long and bad cold. That makes it easier to try to forget.

SEPTEMBER 7, '98

Rita is still here. She's a 24-hour live-in nurse. I asked Chris how much longer she'd be staying. He said he didn't know, but he'd check into it.

It's ok, but she seems to need to go everywhere I go lately. She said that her agency, under direction of the court, has to make sure I'm ok. That's why this is a 24-hour thing. But she knows, and has told her boss, that I really don't need that kind of care. But for now, when I go somewhere, Rita has to come along. It doesn't matter if it's for a walk -- if someone takes me to lunch, or whatever. *(Friends don't like taking her along, because she doesn't pay her way, we have to pay for her.)*

And so, while speaking of paying, I'm still paying for this kind of care, too. It comes directly out of my pocket.

Rita out, Betty in. Got a new nurse today. Can't figure out why this has to go on and on....

OCTOBER 15, '98

Chris told me that, in court, Freda resigned her career today. She was being forced to answer to the court all kinds of questions about all her other clients. So instead she just quit. But she's not off the hook, just out of a job.

He said she came to court with five attorneys representing her. Sounds to me like she (they) had a lot to lose. How else could she interest five of them to come along? Bieler, though, wasn't one of the five. Chris said that the court has appointed a "special fraud investigator" who has been going through all her cases. They are finding a whole bunch of problems.

And what about her attorney friend-- Gary Bieler? He's running for the state legislature; "someone who'll protect our rights." Ever hear that as a campaign slogan? Probably get elected, too!

NOVEMBER 5, '98

I asked Chris if he could check again to see about Betty being here. She and I don't get along too well. She is always hovering over me, and my friends don't care for her too much either. Betty just isn't very friendly and always has to tell me what to do. After 80+ years, I would hope I've got things pretty well figured out by now.

This is not a good relationship, and it's very frustrating to me. I mean, she is around me constantly. Sometimes we even argue. We shouldn't be doing that. I don't want someone in my house who always wants to argue with me. Bailie doesn't argue with me. Chris and Patricia don't argue with me. And I can't even take Bailie for a walk by myself. At least Rita bent the rules some and let me go alone. She always said she'd get in trouble if anything happened to me, but she said she knew I was ok to take care of myself.

I think someone found out that she was doing that, and that's why she was replaced. I hope this, too, can change soon. I'm too old to be arguing with roommates. Probably not good for my health either.

NOVEMBER 7, '98

Chris said he talked with both my attorneys today and they'll see why I'm still getting 24-hour care. They thought it ended already, and that I was just getting visits from time-to-time. Did I fall through the cracks again? At least I'm glad I asked about it.

Chris and Patricia are going back up north today. For a long time they have been dealing with a daughter who has developed cancer. She has a husband and a little girl. I don't know how they've been able to help me so much during all this. And that's not to mention their son who died of cancer last Christmas. The two of them are so strong, but I know they are hurting. They need to go back. They've even had to go back a couple of times during the summer while staying here to help me adjust. I don't know how they do it.

DECEMBER 16, '98

Betty and I are still at it. She can make me so mad sometimes. I try to stay out of her way, but the trouble is -- she won't stay out of mine. I talked to Chris on the phone today and he is trying to be helpful.

He seems to see it like this, but wants things changed, too:

He said: "You know how protective you are of something when it's entrusted to your care; like you are with Bailie. You're supposed to take care of her and make sure she stays well. That means keeping a close eye on her. Or imagine you are charged with taking care of an egg and making sure it doesn't get cracked. I don't think you'd let it out of your sight -- ever. I think it's the same with your caregivers. They are supposed to take care of you and not let anything happen to you while you are in their care. So they don't let you out of their sight -- ever. They don't want to be responsible should anything happen to you while you're under their care. I do not agree with that theory, but I think that is what's happening here."

I said I couldn't agree either; and that Parole Boards release their prisoners (Wards) into society all the time without worrying about what might happen. And when something does -- "Well, that's too bad, but it's not our responsibility." So all I ask is to be let out on parole. "Stop by if you want, or I'll report to a parole agent, but just leave me alone -- please."

JANUARY 13, 1999

I woke up feeling weak, mostly on my left side. I mentioned it to Betty, but she wasn't concerned. She just wanted to argue about something. I couldn't argue back. The morning went by. Later I picked up the newspaper, but dropped it. I couldn't really get a good hold of it.

Betty took me to the hospital.

DATE UNKNOWN

It is so hard to write. I have to be strapped into a wheelchair to keep from falling out. My chair has a tabletop that I can write on. They keep telling me I had a stroke or two and it will take time. I cannot remember the day when I was told this. Maybe someone can write the date here for me sometime.

DATE UNKNOWN

Another stroke they said. I seem to think ok for the moment, but I do not remember much of yesterday or even the many people who come to see me. I get more visitors than most. I spend time in my wheelchair in what they call the front room, but nobody talks to one another. I think most of them cannot talk. I do not have much to say either. Time for lunch. My left arm is no good, at least I can eat with my right. I still have to be tied to the wheelchair so I stay in it. They tie my left leg in, too.

I wonder how long I have been here? Doesn't seem too long.

FEBRUARY 20, '99

A nice older man and his wife came by today. He said his name was Chris and his wife's name was Pat. He said, "Hi Adele, how are you?" I told him I wasn't really sure and everything seems a little strange -- "Could you write your name down for me please? I like to keep track of visitors." He said he'd be happy to.

He tried telling me about how long he and his wife have known me and asked me if I remembered who Bailie was. I said I really didn't know and that I was sorry if I was not much help. He really seems like a nice man. His wife seems very nice, too. They said they had to go back home in a few days, but that they will be back to see me before they leave.

When they left he said, "Maybe we'll see you back home soon Adele."
Do I live with them?

FEBRUARY 22, '99

The nurse said the two people from the other day are here to see you. So she took me outside and we had a nice visit. They said they have to go back home up north, because they have a sick daughter. Well, I hope everything turns out ok for them. They really do seem nice. If things go well they said that they would be back in a couple of months to stay the summer. Nothing has changed for me, the doctor does not know if I will get my strength back or my memory. That doesn't bother me too much though. I guess it would be nice to remember, but it doesn't seem like I am missing anything either.

I heard my nurses talking earlier. They were saying that Mr. Zurillo "went so fast." They were whispering. One told the other he lived only two weeks after emergency heart surgery, and said they hoped I wouldn't feel too badly. I'm not sure; but I don't think I know him. They made sure I was strapped in tight to my chair and wheeled me out and left me in the lobby. I said, "Don't leave me without my paper and pencil. And make sure the paper is taped down tight."

Someone just came walking by to go visiting. They had a cute little dog with them. It had such cute eyes and little black nose. It made my heart flutter. I wonder if I was a dog person?

DATE UNKNOWN

We all just sit around and wait. Maybe tomorrow someone will come to see me. I have to make sure to get their name and have them write it down for me. I found Mr. Zurillo's name. I think that's who the nurses were whispering about. I guess I won't be seeing him either. Not too many people visit anymore.

(*Letter to Adele from Chris after his last visit*)

February 22, 1999

Dear Adele:

My heart goes out to you today. We have had such emotional times together, fun times, sad times and everything in-between. I visited you today at the hospital and in one respect I am somewhat comforted that you do not remember what has happened to you.

You have suffered a stroke that left you paralyzed and with some difficulty in talking. Your memory of the past has been touched and you cannot fully remember friends and family.

I am writing this with the hope that you will fully recover, but should anything happen, I want this note to be a part of your story. There should be some record of all the things that have gone on. I would suspect you would want to know. There might even be a joke for you somewhere in all of this.

The following events are to help fill in the recent history of your guardianship:

The court's investigator has determined that you are missing approximately $65,000.00 since your contact with Freda Luelow and Company.

Freda Luelow is under criminal investigation, not only for her dealings with you, but also for her dealings with a large number of her 65 former clients. Formal charges are expected.

Margaret Doven quickly left town when the investigation into Freda Luelow began. No one knows where she went and her house is abandoned. She is being sought for questioning.

The first judge who did not see what was happening to you has, ironically, lost his eyesight after a very severe sickness. He is no longer serving on the bench.

The two nursing homes owned by the convict have been permanently shut down.

Brian from the TV's investigative staff died suddenly from cancer. He is terribly missed by his co-workers and the community.

Attorney Gary Bieler was successfully elected to public office.

Our circuit court has adopted new rules for reviewing guardianship cases to help prevent what has happened to you from happening to someone else.

The state legislature has introduced new laws to better regulate the activities of legal guardians.

(Need we wonder how Bieler will vote?)

Both Brian and Scott felt this was the best story they ever covered. We all had many meetings about our plan of attack to get this story out quickly; but one question came up to me from them that showed me their total concern. They asked me, "What if we put all this time into doing this story and Adele -- you know she's not that young -- dies during our efforts?" I answered them saying, "A wrong has been done here and regardless of our timing, or Adele's timing, this wrong has to be made right." I think they had that answer before even asking me the question;

they just wanted to see if I saw things the same. So they said, "Let's go with it then." You know the rest.

Adele, someday I hope to give you a list of all the contacts I made trying to get you help. No one seemed to care. No one seemed to have the time. The TV station's people were the ONLY ones who cared. So now you can tell someone who might say, "The media has too much power" that, frankly, they may not have enough. It's funny, after all your stories have been aired on TV, some of those same agencies I called for help and denied it, now want to "look into some of these improprieties." It's a little late for some of these want-to-be heroes to start doing their job. Your true heroes work at the TV station.

So much has happened. I just thought you might someday want to know all this. I wish there was something I could do to help you, but the doctors say the best thing is time. I know your fighting spirit and we cannot wait to see you home again.

As you have always wished, I will keep your diary and all your notes concerning your time under confinement and try to get them printed in an understandable form. I think your desire to educate others to avoid what you have been through is admirable. I'll read it to you when it is done.

Your friends,

Chris and Patricia Zurillo

May 25, 1999

Adele Fraulen passed away in her sleep this evening; within 72 hours of the passing of her good friend, and neighbor, Chris Zurillo.

Adele was alone, with no one at her side. She made no recovery from her many strokes.

Her story will be told.

Jack Carerra

AUTHOR'S POSTSCRIPT

When Chris Zurillo approached me with his story about Adele's plight, I had an initial impression: the events he laid before me were too unusual to fully believe; too unusual for even fiction. But when I confirmed all the facts surrounding her disappearance on December 12, 1997, Adele's story became an event that had to be told. Chris wanted me to write this story, but I thought he should. His passing left me little choice, and he hoped everyone could learn from this tragedy.

We need to learn that there will always be people willing to take advantage of us at any time, whether in our strong times or our weak times. Simply because they are professional business people, trained in their job, should not exclude them from our being cautious of their actions. Many times they may, possibly like Freda Luelow, expect to be a mere fleeting moment in our lives that no one will pay much attention to, or have time to stop.

I do not want to paint professional guardians with a broad brush as being collectively untrustworthy. Those like Freda Luelow and Company can cause the entire guardianship profession to suffer.   In reality, many guardians truly care for the well-being of their clients.   Freda's business peers actually helped the investigation of Adele's case by supplying invaluable inside information on how Freda should have been operating.   Yet, there are certainly a vast number of "Adele's" locked away.

To help us all, this book may spotlight some warning signs to identify others in Adele's situation. Primarily, Adele was alone, without a family, and she possessed a good, continuous income. Even though Adele had a strongly independent personality, that alone did not prevent her demise. Once the court approved of her new future, Adele's independence simply vanished.

We can learn from this case that the court system was not out of reach for someone like Chris who needed to regain its attention. We could all, as non-professionals, consider using the format of the documents presented in this book, those that Chris presented to his court, as templates for our own use. We should feel free to approach the courts as concerned citizens; in much the same way jailed citizens often do.

Adele was a prisoner, yet she could not access the courts like one. Freda and Company made sure that right was taken away. But if **we** still have the right to approach a court to help someone, we should use it.

In this case, Chris had the money to retain a new attorney to start helping Adele. The attorney made sure her new court papers were filed properly and took great care to see that Adele's next court-appointed lawyer acted in her best interest. He was very effective in those areas. If Chris could not have afforded to pay for a new attorney, he may have had no choice but to personally do the work himself.

If you have concerns about an "Adele" you know, set some time aside at your local library. Read your state laws that regulate the activities of guardians. The more you learn about how they should operate, the more you'll be able to recognize if something is wrong. Then, look into your "Adele's" court file. Your newly acquired knowledge of the law will help you identify things that are not right. Once you find a "loose thread" -- **keep pulling; and tell the court all about it !**

Freda had several loose threads that facilitated her downfall. Chris took full advantage of his ability to concentrate on them. He was able to show the court, through the court's own records, that 1) Freda lied about not having a business relationship with Adele before the 7/2/97 court date; 2) Freda lied when she told the court that Adele had no money; and 3) Freda's entire premise concerning her four reasons for Adele to be considered incapacitated were fraudulent. A quick phone call to an understanding electric utility representative helped put an end to Freda's Claim #1 -- that Adele couldn't pay her household bills.

You, too, can make a difference for someone you know. Also, as we all grow older, the memory of Adele Fraulen's story should stay with us as a reminder of the kinds of traps we could fall into.

This story doesn't have a happy ending. It's not a fairy tale; it's reality. Real life does not always allow events to turn out the way we would like. Adele suffered at the hands of others, and her life may have been shortened by the stress she endured.

She was 82; Chris was 74. Adele didn't remember Chris after her stroke, even though their lives had become so closely entwined. Yet, as they had lived, so they died...within hours of each other. Adele and Chris were good friends. Chris knew the meaning of "help your neighbor."

Adele Fraulen paid a heavy price for this story to be told. Even though she and Chris are no longer with us, I'm sure they would have wanted to tell us all:

"NEVER GIVE UP THE FIGHT."

Adele Fraulen
1998

Chris and Patricia Zurillo